"You're still married to me."

Greg followed Christina as she took the dishes into the kitchen. He continued, "After all these years, you've never made a move to get a divorce. And I'd venture a guess that you're still a virgin."

"I really don't think that's any of your business!" The dishes clattered into the sink.

"Ah, but it's true, isn't it? Because you're not the kind of woman who would cheat on her husband, no matter how long he's been gone."

Christina glared at him. "For your information, I take my vows very seriously. Even if it is only a paper marriage."

"Those vows also said 'until death do us part,'" he reminded her.

White Weddings

When true love waits—until the wedding night...

Dear Reader

Welcome to the fourth book in our miniseries, WHITE WEDDINGS.

Everyone loves a wedding, with all the excitement of the big day: bedecked bridesmaids, festive flowers, a bit of bubbly, and all the emotions of the happy couple exchanging vows... Some of your favourite authors will be bringing you all this and more in a special selection of Enchanted™ novels. You'll meet blushing brides and gorgeous grooms, all with one thing in common: for better or worse, they're determined the bride should wear white on her wedding day...which means keeping passions in check!

Happy reading!

The Editors

MARRYING
MR. RIGHT

BY
CAROLYN GREENE

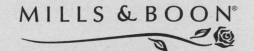

To Bonnie Pega, flower lady extraordinaire.
And to Ernest Irby, my favorite magistrate.

*First published in Great Britain 1999
Harlequin Mills & Boon Limited,
Eton House, 18-24 Paradise Road, Richmond, Surrey TW9 1SR*

© Carolyn Greene 1999

ISBN 0 263 81788 1

*Set in Times Roman 10½ on 12½ pt.
02-9909-43928 C1*

*Printed and bound in Spain
by Litografia Rosés, S.A., Barcelona*

PROLOGUE

"WE'RE here to be married."

Greg's voice was deeper than most eighteen-year-olds', giving him an air of authority that some men twice his age didn't possess. Christina sighed as the warm, vibrant tones surrounded her and melted any fragments of doubt that lingered in her subconscious.

The magistrate flashed a cynical frown at his secretary who passed him the forms they'd filled out earlier. Then he leaned forward and propped his elbows on the cluttered mahogany desk. "Married, eh? I would've figured you for a traffic violation or vandalism."

The man turned to Christina and studied her carefully.

Christina self-consciously pushed back a wind-blown tendril of blond hair and tried to smooth the wrinkles out of her dress. She'd chosen to wear the white sundress because its color fit the occasion, but now she realized it only served to accentuate the differences between her and Greg.

With his deep-set dark eyes and disreputable-looking biker clothes, it was easy to see why he'd earned the nickname, "The Italian Rapscallion." Greg slid his arm around her waist, and for the thousandth time that day—and the millionth time since she'd met him—she felt her heart thudding against her ribs.

As for Christina, with her light hair, fair complexion and eyelet-lace ruffles, she knew she must look every bit the sheriff's daughter. And the homemade rag doll she was holding must have only added to her aura of innocence. She dropped her arm so that the doll hung more discreetly by her side.

Mr. Terby took off his glasses and laid them on their marriage papers. "Do your parents know where you are, little girl?"

She straightened and clutched the doll tighter. "I'm not a little girl," she said, fully aware of the contradiction between her words and the image she was presenting. "I'm eighteen years and one month old, which is legal marrying age in Virginia."

"So it is," he said, putting the glasses back on and straightening papers. "But, as a father myself, I feel it's my civic duty to see that young people don't rush into a decision they may later regret." This time he stared over his half glasses at both of them. "How long have you been engaged?"

Greg looked at his watch. "Two hours." His attitude said, *Wanna make something of it?*

Not a word was spoken for a full minute as each male refused to back down from the other. As always, Christina was amazed at how casually Greg dared to defy someone in such a high position of authority. And she knew from having seen him glare down the school principal and assorted teachers that polyester stretch pants would come in style before Greg would buckle. His refusal to back down from any challenge was one of the many reasons Christina found herself attracted to him.

Finally, Mr. Terby turned back to Christina with a resigned sigh. ''If you and your baby doll are ready—''

''It's not a baby doll.'' Although her words were barely more than a whisper, they captured the magistrate's attention. Now she wasn't sure how to explain why it was so important to include in the wedding ceremony the rag doll she and Greg had made in class. The doll they sewed themselves and were assigned to ''raise'' as their child in the Family Life course at school had sentimental value in their relationship, which was why she'd brought it along for this big event.

Mr. Terby raised one graying eyebrow.

''It's our son, Murdock,'' Greg said without a hint of embarrassment. He didn't bother to elaborate further, even though it was clear he'd snagged the older man's curiosity with his statement.

Greg slanted his gaze at Christina and flashed her a mischievous wink. The simple gesture assured her that—unlike Mr. Terby—he didn't think she was silly or overly sentimental for bringing the memento to their wedding. Although they were as different as two people could be, Christina knew she'd found a kindred spirit in Greg.

Mr. Terby heaved another sigh. ''Very well. Let's get on with it.'' He stood and walked around his desk to a filing cabinet, where he retrieved a thin booklet bound with a narrow gold cord. Then he turned and, grabbing a crocheted loop that dangled high on the wall, pulled down a screen covered with a painted backdrop of a rose-covered trellis. Taking his position in front of it, he palmed his hair to smooth it, then beckoned them to join him.

"Most couples prefer something a little more romantic than an office setting," he said by way of explanation.

While it was a slight improvement over the rest of the book-and-paper-cluttered room, the amateurish artwork with its garish hues of pink and green seemed more tacky than romantic. But Christina preferred not to focus on that. Instead she looped her arm through Greg's as he led her around the desk to stand before the magistrate, and she concentrated on the marital miracle that was about to occur. Greg gave her a smile that took her breath away. She'd never been happier than she was today.

Mr. Terby cleared his throat and began. "Dearly beloved…"

Christina hadn't questioned Greg's motive in asking her to make their pretend marriage real. It was enough that he wanted her. That he made her feel more desirable and more feminine than she ever had in her entire life. That he chose her over all the other, prettier girls at school who openly flirted and clamored for his attention.

"Now place the ring on her finger."

Christina and Greg both looked at each other as if expecting the ring to appear from the sheer strength of their wanting it. In the next moment, Greg surprised her by reaching into his pocket and withdrawing a knife. The muscles in his forearm flexed as he exposed the blade and stepped toward the startled magistrate.

Christina gasped, and the sound was echoed by the secretary who observed the proceedings from near Mr. Terby's desk. The magistrate backed away, as if he were trying to escape down the painted path beneath the trellis.

Greg paused. "Excuse me," he said, motioning the gentleman aside.

Mr. Terby hurriedly complied but stopped short of bolting from the office.

Greg bent and freed the crocheted loop from the pull-down screen, then once again took his place beside Christina. Taking her hand in his, he returned the knife to his pocket and slipped the knotted white threads onto her finger. The fit was a little loose, but the effect was decidedly pretty. Christina held out her hand and admired the makeshift wedding band. Like the man who had put it on her finger, it was untraditional yet appealing.

"Do you take this man to be your lawfully wedded husband?" Mr. Terby once again stood before them, and he seemed anxious to finish the proceedings.

Lawful wasn't a word typically used to describe Greg, but now wasn't the time to argue a point.

After they had finished their "I do's," Mr. Terby added, "I now pronounce you husband and wife. You may kiss the bride, after which my secretary will take an instant photo of the two of you in front of the trellis.''

It was the first time he'd kissed her. Removing the doll from between them, Greg took her in his strong arms and pressed a gentle—almost cautious—kiss on her lips. Upon contact, it was as though everything and everyone in the room ceased to exist. All Christina noticed was the feel of his mouth on hers, the hardness of his muscled ribs against her breasts and the heat of his hands where they splayed across her back.

If a chaste, public kiss from Greg could be this good, then surely a private encounter with him later would be pure bliss. Christina felt as if her heart might explode right out of her chest.

Back in Morrison Heights, Greg led her past the parked cars to the motel room door, which he opened with a plastic key card. He couldn't believe his incredible good fortune. First she'd said *yes,* then she'd said *I do,* and now she was wearing a look that said *I want you.* Before she could go inside, he stopped her with a kiss.

Although his proposal at lunch today had been impulsive and said as a joke, it was rooted in his desire for Christina—his desire to be with her always and continue enjoying the company of the girl who'd captured his heart from the moment he met her.

Instead of laughing at him as he'd expected, Christina had given him a soft smile. ''Are you serious?'' she'd asked. And he'd nodded, still waiting for the laughter that was sure to follow.

The darling of Morrison Heights, she could do no wrong in anyone's eyes—especially not Greg's. She was everything he wasn't, and whenever he was with her, he felt awash with the stability and goodness that were lacking in his own home.

Some people thought he was making time with Christina to annoy her father, who'd taken an instant dislike to him. Sure, he'd love to see the look on Sheriff Cline's face when he and Christina announced their elopement, but he'd want to be with her no matter who her parents were.

To his surprise, the laughter he'd expected upon his impromptu proposal never came. When she'd said yes, he'd been so relieved and happy he'd insisted they tie the knot right away…before she came to her senses and changed her mind.

And now, standing in front of this tacky motel, she returned his kiss with an ardor that equaled his own. It had been clear all afternoon that she wanted him—perhaps almost as much as he wanted her—and it had taken every ounce of willpower to end their wedding kiss and wait until they reached the motel to make love to her. The motorcycle ride here had been sheer torture, and feeling Christina's arms wound so tightly around his midsection had only made his physical discomfort worse. She tilted her head back, staring up at him with his own desire mirrored in her clear blue eyes.

An animal sound escaped from his throat as he

swept her up in his arms and carried her into the room. As he set her down, he reveled in the feel of her body sliding down the length of his own. Pushing a white ruffle off her shoulder, he bent and placed a kiss on her neck. He didn't want to spook her by moving too fast, but when she tipped her head, giving him free access to her bare shoulder, he gave a tug to the other side of her dress.

The white ruffled cloth fell to her waist, baring a simple cotton bra. The old saying was right, he thought. Good things did, indeed, come in small packages.

Kissing her to distract her from the momentary shyness that seemed to overtake her, he slipped his arms around her and deftly released the fastener.

Her breasts were small but inviting, and she didn't flinch from his touch. He knew she was a virgin—she'd told him so when they were working on their Family Life project. She'd said she considered her virginity a gift for the man who would someday be her husband, and he'd fallen even deeper in love with her.

She seemed too good to be true and yet here she was, giving *him*—of all people—her precious gift.

When her small hands fumbled at the hem of his shirt, untucking it from his jeans, desire coursed through him. He peeled off the unwanted clothing in one smooth motion.

In response, she clung to him, her soft flesh flattening against his chest. It was all he could do to keep from backing her onto the bed and having his way with her—hard and fast.

But that wouldn't be good enough for someone as special as Christina. He wanted to unwrap her gift slowly, savoring the anticipation as her treasure was gradually revealed to him. Dropping another kiss on her lips, he told her, "I want you so much."

She sighed, and the motion pressed her closer against his naked torso. "I want you to know," she began, pausing as she obviously groped for the words she wanted to say. "Those vows we said earlier—for better or for worse, in sickness and in health and everything else—I meant every word of it."

Greg nodded silently. He had no doubt that she took her vows seriously, just as he did.

"I'm going to be a good wife to you…in every way. I want to please you. It's my first time," she confessed, "but I want it to be good for you."

Christina snuggled closer to him and rested her head on his shoulder. Greg had just started backing her toward the bed when a banging sounded behind them. Before he could gather his wits, the door was flung open and sunlight spilled into the room.

"Looks like I got here just in time," a male voice boomed.

As Christina stared past Greg, the passion in her eyes was quickly replaced with panic.

"Daddy!"

Greg turned his back to her, shielding her from the questioning gazes of Sheriff Cline, his deputy and the motel manager while she hastily adjusted her clothing.

The uniformed men glared at him in much the same way someone peers distastefully at a bug before squashing it.

"Daddy, before you get the wrong idea—"

"Never mind that, young lady. We'll talk later about you casting your pearls before swine." Sheriff Cline nodded to the deputy, who approached Greg with a pair of handcuffs. "Right now I have a matter of a robbery to discuss with your hoodlum friend here."

Greg didn't resist as the deputy cuffed him and recited his rights. The shame he felt right now wasn't for himself—it was for having put Christina in the middle of this mess.

"You can't do this," Christina insisted, clutching Greg's arm. "He hasn't done anything for you to arrest him."

Greg stood straight, but he didn't meet her gaze. *Couldn't* meet her gaze. "Christina," he said softly, "let the man do his job."

"But you didn't—"

He turned away from her, and he knew she assumed the worst. Not that he blamed her. He should be used to it by now—people always tended to think the worst about him—but it hurt so much more, coming from Christina.

He could try to explain. Try to tell her that the situation wasn't what it seemed, and he was confident she would believe him. But her father wouldn't, nor would anyone else in town, for that matter. He was as good as convicted right now.

She watched in stunned silence as the deputy led him to the patrol car parked outside, slammed the rear door shut and said to no one in particular, ''Looks like this piece of trouble will be off the streets for at least a couple of years.'' Then he threw Greg's shirt onto his lap.

Christina started toward the car, and her father laid a hand on her arm. Breaking free of his grip, she ran to Greg and yanked open the car door.

''I'm going to find someone to help you,'' she declared, even though she must have known that no teacher or other adult in town would come to his defense. ''And while we're getting this straightened out, I'll be there for you…just like we vowed.''

When he could muster the courage to look at her, he tried to steel himself to her beauty and sweetness. He knew with certainty that she would do as she promised—she'd stick by him through better or worse, through thick or thin—but what kind of louse would he be to make her endure such a hell? She deserved more than that, and one day he would find a way to give her the kind of life that was worthy of her. And he'd make *himself* worthy of her, no matter how long it took.

''I'm not going to drag you down with me.''

''It's okay,'' she said as her father approached the car. Her earnestness was sincere. ''I'll wait for you. And I'll come see you every day.''

He had no doubt about that, but such an environment was not for the likes of someone as pure and sweet as Christina. With a stabbing pain in his heart, he knew the only way to protect her from it was to release her from her vows.

Someday he'd come back for her—when he was good enough for her. When she could be proud to introduce him as her husband. In the meantime, though, he had to let her go.

"I don't want you there," he said, his voice hard and strained. "There's nothing left for us. Forget about me, and get on with your life."

In his life, Greg had done a lot of things he wasn't proud of, but he would never forgive himself for making Christina cry.

CHAPTER ONE

YOU make one foolish mistake in your entire life and, sure enough, ten years later he shows up on your doorstep, looking sexier than any man has a right to look. Her body mutinied, urging her to fling herself into his arms and pick up where they'd left off. Wisely, and with great effort, she resisted the urge, and it was just as well that she did.

Greg Primo was not a happy camper.

An official-looking packet of papers dangled from between his large fingers.

She glanced over her shoulder into the living room to see if Donald was aware of what was going on. Fortunately he had his nose buried in the business section of the newspaper.

"What's the meaning of this?"

All those years apart, and no how-do-you-do or my-how-you've-changed. Nevertheless, he still had the power to make her drop everything and turn her full attention to him. It seemed as though her entire body was focused on him. It wasn't just his physical presence although, heaven knows, Greg's muscle-thickened body, almost-black hair and penetrating brown eyes were enough to make any warm-blooded woman from puberty to rocking chair stop and give him her undivided attention.

And right then it would have taken a dynamite blast to divert her gaze from the magnificent human specimen that seemed to fill her front porch. A moth circled crazily as if it, too, were caught in the mesmerizing spell of the man.

As a teenager, Greg had been big for his age. But now…now his shoulders seemed to swell out of the dark suit jacket that was, for him, quite uncharacteristic. In contrast to his torso, his hips seemed narrow in the tailored slacks that hugged his long legs.

No, this was no teenager anymore. And if she weren't convinced by his nearly brutal masculinity, the firm set of his angular jaw told her he was used to getting what he wanted…no matter what it took.

His dark hair fell in casual disarray across furrowed brows. His eyes were deep-set, and his scowling made them appear more so.

He shook the papers at her as if to snap her from her slack-jawed stare back into the present. "Do you have any idea how much trouble this is going to cause me?"

A droplet of perspiration that couldn't be blamed on the late-April weather trickled between her breasts. Christina's gaze traveled down the neatly typed heading on the paper that was now crumpled in Greg's big fist: *Christina Cline vs. Gregorio Primo.*

A movement behind her distracted her from Greg's fury, and when Donald touched her elbow Christina was grateful for the interruption.

"Is something wrong, dear?" He lowered his voice

and spoke into her ear. "Want me to get rid of him for you?"

He was being unusually possessive tonight, acting for Greg's benefit as if he lived here rather than just visited after work and on weekends. And as if their relationship were more than a convenient arrangement to satisfy their respective needs.

The idea of her fiancé taking on Greg was enough to jolt her out of her stupor. She was touched by his unnatural display of machismo, especially since their promises to each other would be in name only.

The two men were as opposite as if they'd come from different planets. Donald was as fair as Greg was dark. At thirty-five, his wispy blond hair was thinning prematurely, whereas Greg's thick brownish-black locks shone under the incandescent porch light. And Greg's tanned six-foot frame dwarfed Donald's medium, deskbound build. Even their attitudes were opposites. Greg's reputation around Morrison Heights was, to put it mildly, less than sterling. And he was full of barely controlled energy, a condition that gave him the appearance of leaning forward even though his posture was perfectly erect. Serious-minded Donald, on the other hand, would someday run for a local political office—with Christina and the children he promised her by his side—and with no fear of any past indiscretions being exposed. His hands hanging awkwardly at his sides, he looked as though he'd rather be reading the stock report than dealing with this unexpected intruder.

"Uh, no, this is..." Her voice trailed off as she

lifted the latch on the screen door and pushed it open. Where was Miss Manners when you needed her? For the life of her, Christina had no idea how one should introduce her fiancé to her husband.

Current husband, that is.

Greg stepped inside, filling the foyer with his massive bulk. How was it that, after all these years, he could still make her heart go *flip-flop?* Christina stepped back in a futile attempt to put distance between them. She would have to broach the subject of their relationship very carefully.

"Donald, I'd like you to meet Greg Primo…an old friend from high school. Greg, this is Donald Winkler, my fiancé."

Greg raised one dark eyebrow. Christina mentally cringed as she waited for something unpleasant to hit the fan. He had just opened his mouth to speak when a rapping sounded at the screen door.

"Greggie, what's taking so long? The mosquitoes are eating me alive out here."

Even in the dark, the woman's platinum-blond hair glowed like a defective nuclear reactor. Christina noticed the barely suppressed sigh Greg gave before he opened the screen door to her. As his companion stepped inside, it was easy to see why the mosquitoes considered her a feast.

She was tall; Christina guessed her height at close to six feet, even without the three-inch heels. But it was the elastic tube top, filled to overflowing and suspended by two narrow shoulder straps, that riveted her attention. The image brought to mind a life-size

Hollywood Heather doll gone amok. Christina tried not to stare in amazement.

Her gaze was drawn upward to the woman's face. It was difficult to tell her age, what with all the makeup she wore, but her bright red smile seemed genuine and friendly.

"It's okay, hon. I get those kinds of looks all the time," the woman informed her.

Christina snapped her mouth closed, certain that her reaction had prompted the announcement.

"Some people think it's too much," the stranger babbled happily on, "but when you're aiming for a stage career, you have to go with the theatrical look." She peered at Christina through her spider-leg lashes. "Maybe we could get together sometime and I'll give you a makeover."

Suddenly Christina felt frumpy. Was that why Greg had changed his mind about staying married to her? Had he been disappointed with what he saw on their wedding day?

No, such a thought was ridiculous. Even so, she self-consciously crossed her arms over her chest. Then, in a burst of nervousness, she uncrossed her arms, captured a strand of hair that had escaped from her ponytail and tucked it behind her ear. Mindful of the grass stains on her knees, she mentally chided herself for not paying more attention to her own appearance tonight. She felt certain her female visitor meant well, but it stung to have it pointed out that she could use some work.

The woman looked up and, apparently noticing Donald's openmouthed fascination, smiled broadly.

"Pardon my manners," she said to Christina, but her attention swiveled to Donald. "I'm Katrina Humboldt, but you can call me Trina. That's my stage name." As she thrust her hand forward, the movement caused her breasts to bobble like overfilled helium balloons.

The action didn't go unnoticed by Donald. He licked his lips and blinked twice. "Pleased to make your acquaintance," he said, taking her hand in his.

Considering the circumstances of Donald's and her unusual marriage arrangement, his enthusiastic response to the bombshell didn't stir any jealousy. But it did make her feel invisible in comparison.

This was getting out of control. She needed to get rid of Greg, and quick. Otherwise, she ran the risk of having her secret exposed, and possibly in a way that would hurt an innocent person. Because her marriage to Greg was over before it had a chance to begin, it had never seemed fully real to Christina, so she had pushed it to the back of her mind. She hadn't purposely withheld the information from Donald. Rather, she had put off telling him since she still felt foolish about having done something so impulsive and uncharacteristic. Now she wished she'd had the foresight to mention it sooner.

Greg cleared his throat. "I hate to break up this touching introduction, but I need to speak to Christina…in private. Excuse us."

At that, he took Christina's elbow in one hand and

placed his other hand at the small of her waist and guided her into the living room where Donald had been reading earlier. Greg's touch was matter-of-fact, but Christina hated how her skin tingled beneath the gentle pressure of his fingers. As if unaware of the conflicting feelings that battled within her, he paused briefly to stare at the watercolor painting of an enormous sunflower that hung over the fireplace. His mouth twisted in distaste. "I hope you didn't pay money for that."

Before she could respond to his slur on her home decor, he pushed past the multitude of houseplants, hesitating only a second to gather his bearings before aiming her toward the kitchen.

Willing a strength she didn't know she possessed, Christina pulled her elbow from his grasp, but he easily maneuvered her into the brightly lit room. It was happening again. He had decided what they should do, and he expected her to go along willingly—to bend to his will—just as she had in the past.

Well, she wasn't a dreamy-eyed teenager anymore, and now was as good a time as any to clue him in. And her traitorous body, too, while she was at it.

As the door swung shut behind them, Christina stepped away and turned to face him. "I don't know what you're trying to prove by barging in here and pushing me around, but I don't appreciate it one bit."

He took the papers out of his back pocket and slapped them against the palm of his hand. "Just as I didn't appreciate getting this little surprise today. Ten years you haven't worried about getting an annulment, and you have to pick *now* of all times to finally go through with it. What have you been doing all this time?''

''I was…''

She caught herself before blurting out the truth. She'd almost said *waiting for you,* which was what she'd subconsciously been doing until recently, when she'd finally given up her childish dream and chosen a more mature arrangement with Donald.

The years had slipped by in a blur, first as she had finished high school and earned her college degree, and then while she'd lived with her parents to save for a down payment on this house. In those early years, she'd been so busy with her goals that she seldom had time to feel the empty ache that had begun with Greg's arrest. But, living on her own the past three years, the loneliness had threatened to engulf her, even as she began spending more time with Donald. Eventually she came to the realization that it was children she needed—caring for them, listening to their laughter, and hugging their cuddly little bodies—to fill the void.

When Donald had offered to give her the children and family life she wanted in exchange for playing the role of a politician's wife, she had readily accepted. In her estimation, it was foolish to be guided into marriage by raging hormones. She'd already made that mistake once. This time she would have a future to look forward to. With Donald.

But she wasn't about to tell all that to Greg. Instead she softly concluded her statement.

"...busy."

The curl of Greg's lip told her the excuse sounded as lame to him as it did to her own ears. He stepped closer, the very proximity of him bringing back the sense of adventure and danger he had instilled in her as a teen. She stood her ground and felt the air fairly prickle with the charge that surged between them.

He had been forbidden to her. He was the dark-haired, dark-souled rebel from the wrong side of the tracks, while she was the fair-haired daughter of the sheriff. She had known then that he was considered wrong for her, but there was something about him that had compelled her to be near him.

Considering the power Greg had held over her at the time—and even now—she conceded their separation had been for the best.

"The lawyer said that since the relationship wasn't...um...consummated, we can get a quick annulment rather than go through a lengthy divorce," she said, trying to get her errant thoughts back on track. "All you need to do is sign the last page."

"No!"

The ferocity of his statement made Christina jump. What was he suggesting? That he wanted to *stay married* to her? That he still had feelings for her? Against her better judgment, she felt inordinately flattered.

But the flattery was short-lived.

"You couldn't have picked a worse time to do this."

Greg yanked a chair out from the table, clattering the wooden legs together in the process, and lowered himself onto the seat. He sat with thighs apart, one knee thrust aside as if in invitation for her to sit on his lap. Christina jerked her gaze upward, forcing herself to focus on the vertical lines between his scowling eyebrows.

"If anyone finds out about this," he continued, "it'll mess up my plans. You're going to have to wait a few months until I have everything in order."

It was bad enough that he'd given her ego a beating, but now he was telling her what to do, trying to bend her to his will as if she were a malleable child.

Although he was seated and she remained standing, he managed to give the impression of power and authority over her. He acted as though, just because he spoke, she must do as he bade. Well, there was no time like the present to show him how much she'd changed since she last saw him. She would refuse to jump at the snap of his fingers…no matter how much she wanted to obey.

She crossed her arms defiantly over her chest. "Can't do it. I'm getting married in two months, and our annulment needs to be final before then."

Christina hoped she sounded more assertive than she felt at the moment. Since they'd been apart so long, and he'd made no attempt to contact her, she had assumed he'd be agreeable to putting an end to their mistake of a marriage. Under the circumstances, his resistance struck her as unreasonable.

She was about to tell him so when the kitchen door swung open and Donald burst into the room. Like a

curious puppy, Trina tripped on his heel, catching herself with a hand on his waist.

"All right, what's going on in here?" Donald
asked.

He was staring straight at Christina, looking to her
for an answer to this relationship mess, so there was
no way Greg could field the question for her. Not that
she'd want him to.

"Well," she began hesitantly, "it's a long story."

"Oh, goody. I love stories," said Trina, making
herself comfortable at the table with Greg.

Everyone waited for Christina to finish her explanation. She turned to Donald, aware that Greg had
risen to his feet. She tried to put her husband out of
her mind and concentrate on how best to tell her fiancé what she had put off breaking to him long ago.

How would she break the news to him without
damaging—or even breaking—their relationship?
Would the knowledge affect the agreed-upon terms of
their engagement? Tension gripped her until it felt as
though she couldn't breathe, and their "audience"
wasn't making matters any easier. She could practically feel Greg's gaze holding her in his grip.

"Maybe we should talk about this in private," she
suggested, attempting to steer Donald out of the
kitchen and away from earshot.

"No, you don't have to whitewash anything for
me," her fiancé said, lifting his chin and squaring his
shoulders as if preparing for a physical punch. "Give
it to me straight."

Donald was a good man…a little intense at times,

but his heart was in the right place. And he'd always treated her with gentleness and respect, not even complaining when she'd insisted on remaining a virgin until their wedding night. In fact, he had admitted to a similar lack of experience and suggested they make a pact to abstain until they were locked in holy matrimony.

Not that doing so was a sacrifice for either of them. In fact, it helped delay what would eventually be—for both of them—a potentially awkward situation.

More importantly, she was still technically married. And since Christina was a woman of her word, she could never bring herself to sleep with a man while married to another…even if it was a marriage on paper only.

"I don't know where to begin."

"Why don't you start by telling your fiancé that you're already married to me?" Greg intervened. His gaze bore into her, and he seemed to be standing much too close, even though they were a respectable distance apart.

"Oh my gosh, this is just like that soap opera, 'A Million Tomorrows,'" Trina piped in. "Only Deiter Hawkins forgot to tell his fiancée about the baby he had by the nun who nursed him through his amnesia." She paused to take a breath. "You two don't have a child, do you?"

"No."

"Yes."

"What?" Donald started to pace, an action generally reserved for times of high stress and low stock reports.

"Not exactly." By now Christina's stomach was knotted with tension. She leaned a hip against the sink and turned a shoulder to Greg in an attempt to discourage him from participating any further in their conversation. But she knew from experience that a simple act of body language would not be enough to silence him if he had something to say.

"A son, Murdock," Greg said over her shoulder. Then, in a wistful tone, he added, "and we had such fun making him."

Christina spun to face her tormentor. "You're not—*hic!*—helping matters!"

"Hiccups again? Why don't you sit down," Donald suggested, "and I'll get you a glass of water."

"Water doesn't help," Greg said. "It's better if you make her laugh."

In all the time she'd known him, Christina couldn't remember hearing her fiancé laugh. Odd that she hadn't thought of that before now.

"No, water's best," Donald insisted, pushing the glass toward her. "We've dealt with her hiccups every day since we announced our engagement, so I ought to know what works best."

"*Hic!*" Christina sat in the chair Greg had vacated a moment earlier. To distract herself from the memory of his open-legged sprawl in that very chair, she started chugging the glass of water.

"And I've seen her through at least a dozen high

school book reports and oral essays, so I ought to know that laughter works best for Christina.''

''It doesn't matter,'' Christina said with a slam of the empty glass on the table. Now that she had their attention, she would attempt once again to tell Donald about her past. *Their* past. ''Now do you want to hear—*hic!*—this or not?''

Trina raised her hand and bounced in her seat. ''I want to hear it. You go, girlfriend!''

Christina took a deep breath. ''Greg and I were assigned to be make-believe husband and wife in our Family Life course.''

''They must've started that course after my time,'' Donald said. ''I never did anything like that.'' Thirty-five years old, he had graduated seven years before her.

''They did. The course was our principal's attempt to teach students about life in the real world. During our role-playing as married couples, we learned to take care of a child, keep a budget, clean house and prepare meals.''

''We took our roles very seriously,'' Greg interrupted with a grin.

He wasn't helping matters at all! ''Actually it was something of an impulse to get married for real.''

Donald said nothing, just taking it all in, but his lack of response made her feel as if she should do a better job of justifying their impetuous decision.

''We were young and foolish.''

Christina had no idea why Greg had been attracted to her or asked to be her class partner. All she knew was that most girls with a normal level of hormones surging in their veins would have given their driver's license for a date with the school hunk who was admired for the "six-pack" of muscled ridges that graced his firm abdomen and his ability to crack walnuts between his biceps and forearms. And yet she had *married* him.

And almost made love to him. She gave an involuntary sigh.

"We were as different as two people could be," she continued.

"You can say that again." Greg addressed Donald as he filled in the rest. "Our teacher, Mrs. Murdock, had agreed to let us pair up for our class assignment. She must have thought Christina's good behavior would rub off on me and keep me out of detention hall."

What would their teacher have thought if she'd seen how Greg's sense of adventure had rubbed off on *her?*

"You still haven't told me about your son."

Donald looked disappointed, as he had every right to be. Surely he must think she had lied when she told him she was a virgin and wanted to remain so until a wedding ring—a *real* wedding ring—graced her finger.

"We had a pact," he reminded her solemnly.

"It's not what you think." She would explain the details of their nonconsummated marriage later, but for now it was more important to set the record straight on the bigger issue. She hiccuped again. "Our so-called son was a rag doll and we were graded on how well we took care of it.''

"Okay, that issue is settled,'' Greg said in an obvious attempt to change the subject. He tapped the papers impatiently against the palm of his hand. "Now let's get back to the divorce.''

"Of course,'' said Christina. "I'll get you a pen.'' Even though she had consciously known it would someday come to this, the finality of a divorce hadn't hit until now. She handed him the pen, trying not to notice the hard calluses on his fingers or imagine what it might have felt like if he'd been given the opportunity to trace those calluses over the rest of her body so long ago.

"I'm not signing.''

"What?''

"I said I'm not signing.''

"I heard what you said. And I believe you also heard me say that Donald and I are getting married in two months.'' She tried, unsuccessfully, to keep the panic out of her voice. "You *have* to sign those papers.''

"That would present a problem,'' Greg said, shaking his head. "You see, I need you to perform a few wifely duties first.''

Stunned, Christina at first met his comment with openmouthed silence. She had seen that determined expression before, and it was obvious he was dead serious about his demand. A sudden urge to flee came over her. She could only assume this was fate's payback for her having indulged in the fantasy of completing their wedding union each night as she drifted off to sleep. Christina backed away from the man who was threatening to wreck her life, stopping only when she collided with Donald.

Her fiancé put his arm protectively around her.

As she recovered from the shock of Greg's demand, her emotions surged into anger. How dare he insult her with such a suggestion…and in front of her fiancé and his own girlfriend, no less!

"Oh, don't worry," Greg assured her as casually as if he were suggesting a walk through the park. "It's not like you have to put your heart in it. All I need is for you to go through the motions."

CHAPTER TWO

IN AN uncharacteristic response, Donald closed the space between them and grabbed a fistful of Greg's white shirt and tie. "I'm going to have to ask you to leave now." He enunciated the words carefully, as if he were Clint Eastwood in a Dirty Harry movie. "You're upsetting my fiancée."

When Greg simply stood there and glowered down at him, Donald grabbed him by the arm and attempted to haul him to the door.

Christina couldn't believe her eyes. "Donald, what are you doing?"

To her surprise, Greg disengaged himself from Donald's grasp. Quickly. In a flash, he had the smaller man pinned against the wall.

"Greg, stop it now! You're hurting him."

"Oh, you lucky girl!" Trina squealed from behind her. "You have two handsome men fighting over you!"

Her comment seemed to make Donald squirm harder, which caused Greg to tighten his hold. "Hey, take it easy on my right hand," Donald protested. "Those are my calculator fingers."

Christina looked around for something to use against the man who had crashed back into her life. There was the crystal wine decanter on the counter,

34

but it had been in her family for years and she didn't want to risk breaking it. Her gaze swept across the kitchen table and fell on the tall wooden pepper mill Trina had been toying with earlier.

She picked it up and, holding it by the top, stepped closer to the two men. She waved it near Greg's face, knowing full well she could never bring herself to hit him, no matter how much he infuriated her. "I'm serious about using this."

He relaxed his hold slightly on Donald and turned an amused grin on her. "What are you going to do...pepper me with blows?"

Then, as if to show how unconcerned he was about her supposed threat, he turned his attention back to the man pressed against the flowered wallpaper. "Your calculator fingers? Are you an accountant or something?"

"A lawyer. But I want to specialize in accounting," Donald said as casually as if they were having a business lunch. "For now, though, I'm starting out in general practice."

Before Christina could work up a steam about being dismissed so offhandedly, Greg released Donald, who rubbed the circulation back into his hand.

"Really?" said Greg. "I'm getting ready to open a new business here in town, and I could use some help setting up my books. Not only that, I have this problem about the lease for the building..."

Before she realized what was happening, Greg had hired Donald as his accountant and legal advisor. The two men shook hands to close the deal.

It was as if they were now the best of friends. Christina doubted she'd ever understand men or their bonding rituals. "Donald, why are you getting involved with him? Have you forgotten what he just suggested to me?"

"Oh, yeah," he said, scratching his head. "That's going to be a problem."

"Actually I only need her for a month or so." Greg straightened his rumpled tie and then shoved his hands into his pockets. "Could be less if the old lady is cooperative."

"*Excuse me,* but this is not just another business deal you two are closing!" She situated herself between the men, placed her hands on her hips and glared up at Greg. "The 'old lady' is standing right here, and she's feeling anything but cooperative at the moment."

Trina looked up from the paper napkin she was folding into a tiny triangle. "You tell 'em, sister!"

Greg actually had the nerve to laugh. "You thought I was referring to *you?*" He heightened the insult by patronizingly cupping her cheek in the palm of his big hand. "The old lady I spoke of is the ninety-three-year-old widow who owns the warehouse I want to rent for my new business."

Christina turned her face away from his warm hand, trying not to think about the last time he'd touched her like that. She needed to get him out of her house—and out of her life. And the sooner, the better. "I don't see what that has to do with me."

"I have a chain of exercise gyms along the East

Coast. When I recently moved back to Morrison Heights, I decided to open one here, too. Mrs. Odell's warehouse is in the perfect location, and it's the right size. The only thing holding up the contract is her need for proof that I'm 'settled' enough to suit her.'' He gave her a charming smile that showed straight, white teeth and a hint of a dimple. ''So I told her I was married. Now she wants to meet my wife. That's you.''

''You own a *chain* of exercise gyms, and she wants proof that you're settled?''

''Well, I am new back in town, and there's that matter of my jail time…''

Donald's eyes widened. ''Hey, buddy, if you were involved in some kind of white collar crime, then you better find someone else to handle your business affairs.''

''Oh, no, it's nothing like that,'' Trina said, rising from the table and tugging at her jeans. ''It was only robbery, and that must have been ten years ago.''

''I know you're trying to help, but you're making it sound worse than it was,'' he told Trina. To Donald, he said, ''It was a case of being in the wrong place at the wrong time, and with the wrong people.''

Greg reached into his pocket and pulled out his keys. ''All I need you to do,'' he said, turning back to Christina, ''is come to Mrs. Odell's town house with me, meet her for tea and look wholesome and settled.'' Almost as an afterthought, he added, ''That ought not to be hard for you.''

Christina wasn't sure whether to take that last part as a compliment or an insult.

"I'd offer to stand in for you," Trina interjected, "but it would be hard for me to tone down my natural 'glam.' You, on the other hand, absolutely reek of reliability and stability."

Greg caught Trina's eye and made a slicing motion across his throat. She, in turn, mimed a locking gesture beside her mouth, then threw away the imaginary key.

Turning back to Christina, he added, "Oh, and you'll have to hold off on the annulment until the lease is signed."

"I can't do that." She stepped closer to Donald and reiterated what she'd said before. "We're getting married, and the annulment needs to be finalized right away."

"Legal notices are publicized in the newspaper. If word of the annulment gets out before the deal is done, Mrs. Odell will sign the warehouse over to someone else."

Christina tilted her chin up. His reappearance had her emotions all topsy-turvy, but she couldn't let him see the power he held over her. She would not bend to his will. "That's not my concern."

"Fine, then I won't sign the papers."

"Then I'll just proceed without you. Donald, I can do that, can't I?"

"Well, it depends—"

"It's not like we ever lived together, and we certainly didn't consummate the marriage."

Donald and Trina spoke in unison. "You didn't?"

Greg remained silent, leaving it to Christina to explain.

"Circumstances intervened." No need rehashing the arrest...or the fact that he had rebuffed her after the honeymoon was interrupted. She'd cried many tears over that, not only because he had rejected her when she'd been trying to live up to her marriage vow of sticking by him for better or worse, but also because she'd been forced to consider the possibility that his intent in proposing had not been for marriage itself, but for the wedding night. And once that possibility had been taken away, he no longer wanted her. She tried with limited success to keep the tremor out of her voice as she spoke. "In retrospect, it's clear that our marriage wasn't meant to be."

"I still don't understand how two healthy, normal human beings could pledge themselves to each other, and then not follow through on the best part," Trina said. "It's a mystery to me."

Christina supposed it was fortunate she hadn't sampled the "best part." As it was now, Donald's and her virginity pledge had kept them from being reckless as they headed toward a permanent partnership. In this relationship there was no crazy rushing into marriage, no frantic clinging to each other while yearning for bodily delights. No, this was a much more mature relationship, one that allowed them to exchange chaste kisses without the desperate urge for sexual release. This impending union was nothing at all like the first, and she took that as a good sign.

When the time came—*after* the ''I do's'' and when they were ready to start a family—they would proceed calmly and maturely to the marriage bed.

''So I don't need Greg's signature in order to proceed, do I?'' she prompted.

''No, I don't think so.'' Frowning as he mulled over the particulars, Donald absently rubbed his Adam's apple. ''It may take slightly longer, getting witnesses to say that you've lived apart all these years and never slept together, but an annulment should be fairly quick and easy.''

''True,'' Greg agreed, ''but a divorce can be long and dragged out, especially if it's contested.''

His deep voice rumbled seductively, and Christina had the feeling he practiced that tone often to get what he wanted. She suspected his success rate was high.

''But we don't need to go through a divorce since the marriage was never consummated.''

''According to *you,* it was never consummated, but I might have something different to say about the matter.''

''You wouldn't!''

''Go along with me until the lease is signed,'' he said with a smile, his voice deceptively light and coaxing, ''and I won't have to.''

''He's like that in his business dealings, too,'' Trina announced proudly. ''He just won't take no for an answer.''

That was certainly the truth. Christina had never known him to give in easily, especially if he wanted something badly enough. Why, look what measures he'd gone to after he had set his sights on her. Sure, lots of girls at school would have succumbed to his charms—and probably had—but Christina had wanted even then to take her virginity to the altar. After ten years of reflection, she could only guess that marriage had been merely an obstacle to overcome in his quest to bed her.

She turned to look at her fiancé. In light of his easygoing nature and relatively calm reaction to tonight's turn of events, she guessed he would probably go along with Greg's request...not that they had much choice. But it was only fair to offer him a say in the matter.

"Donald?"

He dropped his hands to his sides and stepped away from her as if he were already turning her over to Greg. "I suppose if it's only to have a cup of tea with an old lady, there wouldn't be any harm in that."

Donald was such a gentleman, and Christina felt lucky to be engaged to him, even if theirs was a rather odd arrangement. So why did she feel disappointed that he didn't raise at least a little fuss?

"No, I suppose there wouldn't," she reluctantly agreed. But something in the back of her mind whispered that where Greg was concerned, there was always the potential for danger.

"Good, then it's a deal." Greg stretched out his hand to Christina. After a moment's hesitation on her part and his joking reassurance that no buzzer lay hidden in his palm, she slipped her fingers into his.

Once again, Greg had managed to get her to bend

to his will. Feeling manipulated and used, she clenched her teeth. She may have been railroaded into the deal, but she was determined to get it over with as soon as possible.

He held her hand in his grip for a mere second longer than necessary, gave a firm but meaningful squeeze, then abruptly let go as he turned to Donald and clapped him on the shoulder. "Thanks, pal. I appreciate your understanding."

"No problem," Donald said.

Then, to Christina, Greg added, "I'll pick you up at three-thirty on Sunday for tea at Mrs. Odell's." He looked her over, his gaze settling on the grass-stained, faded jeans and overlarge T-shirt. "And wear something nice." Greg gave her a devilish wink. "Maybe a white sundress."

Donald was wrong. This definitely would be a problem.

Christina had just stepped out of the bathtub and into a clean top and pair of jeans when the doorbell rang.

"Be right there," she hollered.

With a prolonged sigh, she pulled a wide-toothed comb through her wet hair. It wasn't like Donald to show up unannounced after work unless he'd had a bad day. During those times, he would spout off whatever difficulties he'd incurred at his struggling law practice and then spend the rest of the evening unwinding in front of her television.

Well, she'd had a rough day, too, and tonight she just didn't know if she could summon the encouragement and smiles he would need to put him back in his usual good mood.

It wasn't so much the physical exhaustion that came with the job of landscape designer, though that certainly played a part in her frustration. Mostly it was her supervisor, Linda, who had the annoying habit of sending her out on jobs that any of the groundskeepers could have handled. The reason? Because "you have a knack for dealing with difficult customers," Linda had said, expecting her to be so flattered she'd drop the argument. But today she hadn't dropped it.

Maybe it was because of the run-in she'd had with Greg the night before, or perhaps a hormonal fluctuation, but today she'd eloquently and insistently pointed out that as the landscape designer, that's what she intended to do hereafter…design. Routine lawn and plant maintenance would have to be left to the staff hired for that job, no matter how difficult the client might be.

Christina didn't know if her adamant stance would have an effect on her supervisor, but it had certainly taken the other woman by surprise.

She crossed the living room and reached for the doorknob. Regardless of the result, she needed to do some decompressing and unwinding, herself. And she would start with a trip to the Salad Hut for dinner.

"Hi, I was just going to…" The rest of the sentence hung in her throat as she opened the door and saw not Donald, but Greg standing on her porch.

The image before her was closer to the memory

she carried of her teenage groom than the man she'd seen a few nights before. The black jeans reminded her of the rebel he'd once been, and the close-fitting, pectoral-hugging pullover shirt reminded her of one reason she'd said yes to his impetuous proposal. The difference was that he was now bigger, older and more in control…not only of himself, but also of those around him. And the fading pink scar on his cheek hinted that he was still willing to do whatever was necessary to retain that control.

"You're going to the warehouse with me," he finished for her and then gave her a quick once-over. "You don't have to change…you look fine."

Despite their years apart, a compliment from Greg still unnerved her…made her self-conscious, yet eager to please. How was it that he held such power over her? She tried to make herself immune to his charms, which was about as likely as the tide making itself immune to the pull of the moon. Even so, she ought to at least *appear* invulnerable.

"Excuse me?" she said evenly.

"No need to apologize. It could happen to anyone," he said with a devilish grin. "Cucumbers for lunch?"

"I didn't— You can't just—"

"Yes, I can. Mrs. Odell gave me the key for a final walk-through before we draw up the lease. Since we're going to meet with her this weekend, I thought we'd be more believable as a married couple if you'd already seen the place and could make a few knowledgeable comments about it."

"Well, I suppose you're right…"

"Of course I'm right. Now grab your purse and we'll be on our way."

He was doing it again—bursting into her life and trying to turn it upside down with a smile and a snap of his fingers. She'd already blown up at her supervisor today, and she wasn't about to let herself be manipulated by a husband—a soon to be *ex*-husband—that she hadn't seen in ten years. No matter how handsome he might be.

"Look, I haven't even had dinner yet, and I was planning to—"

"Don't worry about dinner. It's on me."

Dinner would indeed be *on him* if he persisted in being so pushy. But then she considered her options. She had been left with no choice in the matter of meeting with Mrs. Odell and playing the part of Greg's devoted wife. Perhaps, as he had suggested, touring the warehouse with him would help pave the way to a quicker signing of the lease…and a quicker annulment. Even the mere thought of forever signing him out of her life made her breath catch in her throat. But she had to steel herself and do whatever it took. In the long run, it would be better for both of them.

She turned her attention back to the matter at hand. If they left the car window down, her hair would dry before they reached the restaurant. She left him at the door while she went to retrieve her purse.

"You still like veggies, right?" he asked upon her return. "I hear they have a great Wednesday night special at the Salad Hut."

Whatever annoyance she'd felt toward him until now was diminished with that one observation. After all these years, he'd remembered her favorite food.

The warehouse sat in a formerly neglected pocket of town. Previously used to store furniture, the building had fallen into disrepair when Mrs. Odell's husband became ill fourteen years ago. Then, after the furniture company tenants moved out, the structure languished as the elderly woman struggled to recover from her husband's death. In recent years, however, many of the old homes around the building had been sold and renovated as offices or torn down to make room for restaurants and quaint retail shops.

The neighborhood was on the verge of an economic comeback, Greg had told her at dinner, and he wanted to sign the lease before competing business owners discovered its potential.

He turned the key and motioned for her to enter ahead of him. When Christina stepped inside and the lights snapped on, they were met with construction clutter as far as the eye could see.

"Mrs. Odell's been making some repairs," Greg explained. "New roof because the old one leaked, and now she's having the water-damaged floors and walls fixed or replaced."

Grabbing her hand, he led her around a stack of lumber and waved an arm toward the entry area.

"The reception desk could go here, and offices along that front wall," he continued. "Then this large open area will be the weight room."

He fell quiet, obviously waiting for her comment—or maybe even her approval.

Christina tried to picture what it would look like once the exercise equipment and better lighting were installed. After a moment, she merely said, "I don't know."

"You don't know?" Greg turned to face her. "Can't you see what a prime location this is? Imagine office workers coming here to work out during their lunch break, folks stopping by to pump up before meeting a client for dinner at one of the nearby restaurants and weekend shoppers squeezing in an hour of fitness between errands."

"You're definitely right about that," she agreed. "But maybe you should consider a few alterations if you want customers to keep coming back."

He stepped over some scattered nails and offered Christina a hand as she maneuvered past the mess. "Such as?"

Her hand seemed to burn in his, and she felt guilty for allowing him to have such an effect on her. Self-consciously, she pulled free of his grasp and pocketed her hands in her jeans as he led her into what would one day be the weight room.

"Well, for starters, the yard could use some work," she said, trying desperately to keep her thoughts focused on Greg's business venture…and off Greg. "The walkway is roundabout and inconvenient to the parking lot, and some grass and a few shrubs would make the place look more inviting and less like a haunted warehouse."

She met his gaze and found it necessary to shield her eyes against the harsh fluorescent overhead lighting.

"Consider it done." He didn't seem offended by her suggestions, and she was emboldened by his encouragement. "Go on…"

"The weight room."

"Yes?"

"It's in full view of anyone entering, leaving, or simply standing outside on the sidewalk. If I was exercising in here, I wouldn't want to be seen by everyone who happens to pass by." She motioned behind them. "A pair of double doors between here and the receptionist's desk would block the view and provide privacy."

"Hmm, you have a point there," Greg said, appraising her with a slight tilt of his head. "If people saw you working out, the women would get jealous and leave, and the men would stampede in here and overstay their welcome."

"You don't need to use your golden tongue on me," she reminded him even though she basked in his honeyed words. "I've already promised to have tea with you and Mrs. Odell this weekend."

"Just stating a fact," he said simply. "You're beautiful, Christina." His voice stroked her as surely as if he had touched her with his hands.

Christina's hands came out of her pockets, and she started smoothing her hair. With its natural waves, it always looked unruly, so she didn't know why she bothered. "Um…"

What had she been about to say before he started looking at her the way a lion watches an antelope?

"And the lighting should be softened to give it a more relaxing atmosphere."

"Mmm, dim the lights," he said, breaking eye contact and allowing her to pull air into her oxygen-deprived lungs. She hadn't realized she'd been holding her breath. Greg stepped away for a moment, turned off one bank of lights and returned to casually lay an arm around her shoulders. "Better?"

Against her will, Christina's thoughts rushed back ten years when they'd stood together like this in front of the magistrate. At the time, she'd been acutely aware of the firmness of his biceps pressed against her shoulder and the rigid strength of his chest and abdomen where her arm had touched him.

Some things just didn't change over time…except maybe for the better. And it bothered Christina that she should enjoy the touch of what seemed to be a perfectly innocent gesture. Her response served to remind her of the maturity of her relationship with Donald. Nothing like this would happen if her fiancé were standing here in Greg's place.

She eased herself out of his embrace and felt herself pull in another full breath. It was ridiculous for a twenty-eight-year-old woman to be reacting like this, no matter how intriguing that scar near his left eye happened to be. In an effort to shift their attention to more neutral ground, she pointed to the front wall opposite the proposed offices.

''Perhaps you could use that area for a baby-sitting room.''

Although his dark eyes acknowledged her retreat, he made no move to close the distance between them. Christina pushed aside the illogical sense of disappointment that lodged in her gut.

''Kids,'' he said. ''I hadn't thought of that aspect.''

Greg turned away from her to study the area she'd pointed out. Despite the dim lighting of the room, Christina was afforded a magnificent view of the back of his dark jeans, where the denim pulled taut across his slim hips. If she were a betting woman, she'd wager his gluteus maximus muscles were as hard as his biceps. He turned around, replacing the view with that of his zipper.

''How many children?'' he asked as if he were offering to give them to her himself.

Christina jerked her gaze upward and found him wearing a knowing grin. She felt herself blush, wondering if he'd been able to read her thoughts.

''Would room for four be enough,'' he asked, ''or do you want more?''

When she spoke, her voice was husky. ''More.''

''You want more,'' he confirmed.

Christina licked her dry lips.

Greg cleared his throat. ''Me, too.''

Silence hung in the room. Christina didn't know when or how it happened, but suddenly it seemed as though they weren't talking about the exercise gym anymore.

Greg certainly had a knack for pulling such

switches on her. They had started out as classroom partners and ended up as married partners. More recently, their agreement called for having tea with Mrs. Odell, and then it grew to include a pre-tea tour of the warehouse. And now she didn't know where he was leading with this conversation, but it seemed a wise move to turn it back to business, as the original intent had been.

"It's still a new venture," she suggested, "so it's not like anything is set in stone. Change is to be expected at this point."

He nodded almost imperceptibly. "My thoughts, exactly. We shouldn't be surprised if things don't go as originally planned."

Once again, they seemed to be talking on two different levels. Despite their enjoyable dinner and the interesting flow of ideas for the gym, she was beginning to doubt the wisdom of coming with him tonight. True, he hadn't given her a choice, but it also didn't discount the fact that she was engaged to marry someone else…someone who would be there for her ten years from now.

"I suppose we ought to get back soon." She crossed her arms over her chest, knowing as she did so that it looked like the defensive gesture it was. "Donald's probably wondering where I am."

"Of course." Greg offered her his arm as they retraced their steps over the scattered construction materials. "He should be one of the first to hear of the changes in our plans."

Christina paused as he tugged the door open and held it for her. "*Our* plans?"

"Whatever," he said with a smile, and closed and locked the door behind them.

On Sunday, Greg arrived before Christina had a chance to check her reflection in the mirror. If she peeked now and the results were hideous, she couldn't leave him standing at the door while she scrubbed her face free of the makeup Trina had applied just moments before. So she decided to just take a chance.

Her father always said the best defense was a good offense, so she fired a question at him as she opened the door.

"Did you send your girlfriend over here to make me…presentable?"

Greg took one look and stopped in his tracks. He seemed dumbfounded by what he saw, and Christina immediately assumed the worst. A mental vision of garishly painted lips, clownish red cheeks and hooker-black eyes leaped to her mind.

She put her hands to her face. "What? Is it too much?" Standing on tiptoe, she strained to see herself in the tiny decorative mirror behind the candle sconces on the wall.

"No, *you're* too much," Greg said as he moved to stand behind her. He placed his hands on her shoulders as they both peered at the stunning reflection before them. "You were pretty before," he said, his voice even huskier than it had been on their wedding day, "but you're beautiful now."

As she studied the vision in the mirror, Christina was immediately contrite for assuming the worst about her new friend's makeup skills. The artwork was so subtly done with peach tones and neutrals that it was hard to tell Christina was even wearing makeup at all. But the difference it made was enormous.

"You look like yourself on a good day," Greg told her, his breath caressing her ear. "A *very* good day."

Uncomfortable with the direction their conversation was going, Christina turned to face him, shifting her shoulders to free herself of his disconcerting touch. "You didn't answer my question."

"What girlfriend are you talking about?"

Did he have so many he couldn't keep track of them? "Trina, of course. Who did you think I meant?"

"You have it all wrong. Trina's my secretary and girl Friday."

Christina didn't say anything, but she didn't have to. Her expression spoke for her.

"What? You don't believe me?"

"You don't even have an office yet," she said, stating the obvious.

"Actually she's *going* to be my secretary. I met her when she was finishing her last singing gig. The secretary job is just temporary until she gets her career back on track."

Christina shouldn't have been surprised by that revelation. She hadn't figured Trina for his type of woman—she seemed a bit flamboyant, even for a wild man such as Greg—but she sure didn't fit her image of a professional secretary, either.

"So her first assignment was to make sure I don't embarrass you?" Humiliated, she hung her head. To tell the truth, her confidence had taken a nosedive the moment Greg's friend had suggested that she "do something" about her appearance.

Greg curled a finger under her chin and lifted it until she was looking him in the eye. "The makeover was Trina's idea. I only encouraged her because I thought you might need a little lift—something to boost your confidence—for when you meet Mrs. Odell this afternoon."

"And because it would be hard for Mrs. Odell to imagine you being married to a plain-Jane like me," she quietly finished for him.

She'd thought that back in high school, too. Why would someone as wild, exciting and desirable as Greg Primo be interested in the tame, sedate sheriff's daughter?

"No, that's not true at all." He took her by the arms and guided her to the living room where he sat knee-to-knee with her on the couch. "You are so incredibly pretty—without even trying—that it makes all other women envious."

Trina had told her essentially the same thing earlier, confessing that if she herself weren't going back into show business, she'd want to look exactly like Christina.

Trina had also given her opinion of her employer,

describing him as a saint, which was the last word Christina's father—and most of the Morrison Heights community—would have used to describe the Italian Rapscallion ten years ago. Considering his obvious success in business, however, he'd apparently made a complete turnabout.

She was glad for him. Glad he'd found a way to channel his wayward energy into such positive outlets. Glad he'd finally found his place in society. And once she helped convince Mrs. Odell he was "settled" enough to be a responsible tenant, he would soon carve out a niche for himself in Morrison Heights as well.

And then Christina would be free to carve her own niche...with Donald.

The clock in the hall chimed, alerting them it was time to leave for their appointment.

"I suppose I should change back into the brown suit I wore to church," she said. Apparently unaware of the hidden meaning behind such a choice, Trina had obstinately insisted that she wear the pale peach sundress. And when the younger woman had pushed it into her arms, Greg's offhand suggestion to wear a white sundress had come rushing back at her. The ruffled white dress she'd worn to their wedding had been packed away and stored in her parents' attic because she couldn't bring herself to wear it again after Greg was arrested and refused to see her. The closest thing to it was the plain peach garment that Christina now wore. "After all, we will be discussing business matters."

"That's all the more reason you *shouldn't* wear a suit," he said. "Do you want Mrs. Odell to see you as a hard-edged businesswoman, or as the sweet little feminine woman that I can't keep my eyes off?"

She squirmed under his perusal. Christina knew he was speaking hypothetically, but his comment sounded a little too real for her comfort.

"Well, neither actually…"

Her biggest fear was that one or both of them might start taking this play acting too seriously, as they'd done before.

CHAPTER THREE

MRS. ODELL got straight to the point. "So what did you steal?"

Greg attempted to balance the fragile china cup and saucer on his knee and almost succeeded in dumping the contents on his lap.

Christina knew the story, but he still hated to talk about it in front of her. He'd never tried to hide his past, but he sure would like to move beyond it. Even so, he could understand the older woman's need to know that he was trustworthy.

"I was barely eighteen at the time and was driving some friends around one night. They wanted to stop at a convenience store for some cigarettes, so I waited outside in the car." The story came out woodenly, the result of having to retell it to every potential employer, loan manager and landlord he'd ever encountered. "When they came running out with stolen cigarettes and a handful of cash, I was going to make them give it back. But the store clerk ran out waving a gun, and I panicked and drove off."

"And you got thrown in jail because you were the getaway driver," Mrs. Odell finished for him.

"Or so it seemed."

"Hmm." Apparently satisfied, that was all she said about the matter. "You're not drinking your tea."

He hated tea. He plunked another couple of sugar cubes into the cup to disguise the taste, but the action garnered him a splash of the brown liquid on his slacks.

The casual polo shirt, khakis, and deck shoes had been Trina's idea. ''Mrs. Odell has seen your business side,'' his secretary had said, flicking his red tie with her lacquered nail. ''Now it's time to show her your personal side.'' Well, if he'd done that, he'd be wearing the cutoff shorts and T-shirt that he liked to exercise in.

But his intention today wasn't to show Mrs. Odell the truth. It was to show her what she wanted to see…a conservative, happily married man. The conservative part hadn't been too difficult so far, but Christina was not exactly cooperating on the ''happily married'' end of things.

Not for the first time this afternoon, she caught his eye. Leaning forward, she flashed him a pertinent smile and dabbed a napkin at the tea stain on his knee. She smelled fresh and outdoorsy…like honeysuckle.

She'd always been gorgeous in a healthy, wholesome sort of way. Today, she was all that and more. The demure blue eyes seemed somehow more vivid, her hair more touchable and her lips more temptingly kissable.

He had planned to come back and try to pick up the broken fragments of their marriage after he'd redeemed himself. But it had taken time—much more time than he'd originally anticipated.

First, there had been the jail time to serve, then

he'd worked as a garage mechanic and tapped investors until he'd collected enough money to open his first exercise gym. Success had come quickly after that, but not quickly enough to suit him. With each new gym he opened, with each step he advanced up the ladder of success—and, ultimately, with each notch he rose on the scale of respectability—he was always focused on one goal. Winning Christina back.

The next step in his plan, even before trying to win her back, had been to earn a place of respect among the people of Morrison Heights. Never again would he risk clouding her crystal reputation by merely associating with her. And if that meant opening a gym here, serving on the Chamber of Commerce and donating to charities, then he was prepared to do whatever it took.

What he hadn't been prepared for, though, was getting the annulment papers while he was in the homestretch of earning the community's respect and thus becoming a suitable match for the town's darling.

He grasped Christina's hand in his and held it as a loving husband might touch his beautiful wife. In reality, he feared that if she continued dabbing at the tea stain on his pants, he'd wind up showing Mrs. Odell more of his personal side than he'd intended.

"Look at you two lovebirds," exclaimed Mrs. Odell. "It's hard to believe you've been married almost ten years."

Christina pulled back and folded her hands primly in her lap. If she kept this up, she'd undo all that he'd managed to accomplish to this point.

"Another biscotti?" The elderly woman pushed the almond abominations at him, and Christina happily accepted two—one for each of them. She nibbled hers, watching out of the corner of her eye to see if he would follow suit. Begrudgingly he dunked the hard-as-brick cookie into his tea to soften it. When he bit into it, he was even more repulsed, but he struggled valiantly not to show it. That was when Christina's demure expression broadened into a bright smile.

She had set him up!

"You two remind me of the way Clarence and I were at your age." Mrs. Odell seemed oblivious to the subtle underplay that was going on between them. "We were so in love. Why, we could hardly keep our hands off each other."

Greg set his cup on the table, then sidled a little closer to Christina. Payback time! "I know what you mean," he said, sliding one arm around Christina's shoulders and giving her a squeeze. "Chrissie and I have the same problem."

"Chrissie?" Christina leaned away from his embrace. "When did you start calling me that, *Greg-gums?*"

Mrs. Odell put a hand to the gold locket at her chest and sighed. Then she stood abruptly and picked up the teapot. "My goodness, it looks as though we're nearly out of tea. You wait here while I make some more."

Christina sat up straighter. "Do you need any hel—?"

"Thank you," Greg said and nudged Christina with his elbow. "We'd love some more of your delicious tea."

When she was gone, Christina lightly pressed the palm of her hand against the center of his face.

"What was that for?"

"Just pushing your nose back in, Pinocchio." She flattened her lips together and made him think once again about kissing her. "Is that how you conduct all your business dealings—through pretense and subterfuge?"

He shrugged. "Subterfuge would imply an evasion of some sort. I think pretense is a better description."

"Or how about lying?" she suggested, her voice rising right along with her indignation. "I don't like what we're doing to that sweet old lady, Greg, and I'm calling a halt to this deception. When she comes back in here, I'm telling her the truth."

On that last word, she gave him a self-righteous little nod, as if the matter were settled once and for all.

Her do-right attitude was part of what had attracted him to Christina those many years ago, and he still admired her honesty and integrity. But now, with so much riding on this meeting, was not the time to have a fit of conscience.

"Need I remind you of our agreement?"

She rose from the love seat they'd shared and stood over him, her hands on her curvy little hips. "It was stupid of me to even consider going along with your scheme, much less actually participate in it. I'm not going to be your pawn anymore.'' She reached for her purse. ''In fact, I'm not even going to wait for Mrs. Odell to come back in here. I'm going to tell her now.'' She raised her head defiantly. ''And then I'm leaving.''

She made a move toward the kitchen, but Greg caught her arm before she could make good on her promise. He remained seated, which better enabled Christina to look haughtily down her nose at his fingers, which almost closed around her slim upper arm.

''And what about your wedding?'' he reminded her. ''Won't it be a lie when you promise to 'forsake all others' even though you'll still be legally married to me?''

His words apparently hit their mark. She hesitated, and when she spoke again she didn't sound quite so cocksure of herself. ''My father always said that if you do what's right, the details will somehow take care of themselves. Now, if you'll let go of my arm—''

The kitchen door swung open. Reacting instinctively, Greg gave a tug so Christina would return to her seat beside him, but the motion caught her off guard, her purse went flying and she ended up sprawling atop him. When she opened her mouth to protest the unexpected roughness, he abruptly silenced her by covering her lips with his own.

The words she'd been about to utter were released as a moan as he slid one arm around her back and pressed her closer.

She had stopped her fall with her hands braced

against his chest. To his surprise and immense plea-sure, one small hand moved behind his neck and the other went under his arm to cup his shoulder. In doing so, Christina seemed to melt against him, her soft warm breasts pressing gently against his chest.

After the initial shock, Christina felt herself surren-dering to his kiss. She'd forgotten how good he smelled, how hard his body felt against her own, and how the touch of his lips could make her forget ev-erything else. Everything but the awareness that a kiss from Greg Primo—incredible as it was—only repre-sented the tip of the iceberg. And, against her will, she found herself wanting to go below the surface to discover the rest of the pleasures that he surely held for her.

To her immense regret, his firm embrace relaxed and the tea-sweetened taste of his mouth against hers grew faint as he gently pulled away.

Christina opened her eyes—her mind a happy, fuzzy blur—and gazed into his dark brown irises. But his attention was elsewhere, focused on some-thing…or someone…beyond her left shoulder.

"Oh my, you two really know how to keep the honeymoon alive, don't you?"

Christina's wits returned with a slam into the log-ical, do-right side of her brain, and she scrambled to climb off Greg with as much dignity as she could muster and return to her seat. What had she been thinking?

Mrs. Odell set the teapot on the table in front of them as Christina simultaneously smoothed her dress and tried to slow her breathing. "Don't mind me. I'm all in favor of young love."

"But we're not—"

Greg stilled her with a warning scowl.

She thought about the upcoming wedding and Greg's threat to throw a kink in the annulment by claiming they'd consummated their marriage. Maybe, as her father had said, the details would work themselves out if she followed the high road, but with so little time before the wedding, she knew she couldn't take that chance. Christina cleared her throat and placed her hands palms-down on her lap. "—we're not usually so, um, bold."

"Honey, don't you worry a bit about that." Mrs. Odell refilled their cups before continuing. "A person sees more than that on television nowadays."

The elderly woman passed them their cups, and Christina almost smiled at Greg's response. He was clearly not happy about the prospect of downing another cup of tea. She gave an audible sniff. Served him right—first for deceiving a kindly old lady, and then for that heated seduction.

"I'm sure you two want to go home and maybe have a little candlelight dinner," Mrs. Odell said, sounding almost wistful, "so I suppose we ought to get on with the business of our meeting today."

As Mrs. Odell and Greg launched into the particulars of the warehouse lease, Christina knew his plan had succeeded. He had gotten what he set out to accomplish. And she, despite her wishes to the contrary, had helped him. Just as he'd done ten years ago, he'd talked her into doing something that was against her better judgment.

Well, this current partnership was not going to have a ten-year afterlife, as the other had. As he arranged to meet with Mrs. Odell's lawyer to sign the papers the next morning, Christina knew that this would have to be her final contact with Greg. As for the annulment, her attorney could contact him if necessary. What had occurred between her and Greg on the love seat this afternoon—and her reaction to it—was enough to convince her that the less contact with her soon-to-be-ex-husband, the better.

After he dropped her off at her house this evening, the door would close between them…for good.

Christina stood back and stared in stunned awe at the magnitude of the damage she'd caused. The jagged horizontal rip in the porch screen must have been at least three feet wide, ending with a downward slash that reached almost to the floor.

The hole was her own fault, of course, but lately Christina had been feeling like the victim of some sort of conspiracy. She tugged the towering banana plant and pot away from the rip and then rubbed her hands on her shorts. It seemed as though Greg's reappearance had triggered a run of bad luck in everything she did lately.

Fortunately her contact with him was finished. Now that she had fulfilled her end of the bargain and Greg had the warehouse lease all wrapped up, they could proceed with the annulment. And Christina could finally close that chapter in her life and move on to the next.

In the meantime, summer insects, intrigued by the opening in the screen, were finding their way inside. If she didn't do something soon, they would start making themselves at home among the jungle of plants on her side porch.

Thirty minutes later, Christina had returned from the hardware store with a section of screen large enough to patch the hole.

''I wish it were this easy to keep *all* the pests out of my life,'' she grumbled as she poked a white thread through a sewing needle. This wouldn't be the most attractive patch job, but it would serve a functional purpose until she was ready to enclose the porch in floor-to-ceiling windows for a bright yet sheltered sunroom for her plants.

Pushing the needle through the screen and patch, she tried to angle it inward for the next stitch. Unfortunately the stiff new material refused to give enough to accomplish the simple movement.

With a sigh, Christina pushed it through to the outside, trudged to the yard to pull the thread through and then pushed the needle back in to return to the porch and begin the process all over again. As she did so, tiny bits of the old mesh crumbled in her hands.

She'd made about five such stitches when Greg's car pulled into the graveled driveway. So much for closing the chapter and moving on.

He stepped from the car, gingerly balancing a large white bakery box in his arms.

Christina dropped the sewing needle, letting it swing from the unfinished screen patch as she watched him make his way up the flagstone path. "I thought you'd be busy at the warehouse, getting everything in order for moving in."

"First things first," he said. "I wanted to stop by and thank you for convincing Mrs. Odell you're head-over-heels in love with me."

His devastating grin, coupled with what he'd just said, almost sent her sprawling backward into the hedges. And then she remembered he was referring to their play acting. Her shocked response had her wondering if, perhaps, his words had hit a little too close to the truth. Was she still—maybe a little?—in love with him?

No, of course not! Until two minutes ago, she was ready to move on with her life—without Greg. This was just further proof of his power to make her dangle like a puppet while he controlled the strings.

"Your mother dropped this off with Donald, who asked me to bring it to you since I was coming by here anyway."

Christina took the box from Greg. Their hands touched, and she pulled back as if she'd been pricked by a thorn. To cover her awkwardness, she hastily set the box on the small wrought-iron table.

She looked from Greg to the cake box and back again and tried to lighten the tension that crackled between them. "More wedding cake samples to choose from. My mother's driving me nuts with all these wedding decisions.''

It was clear Greg noticed how she had flinched from his touch. It wasn't so clear, however, whether his laugh came from her reaction or from what she had said. ''Donald says plain old yellow cake is fine with him.''

''That's what I told Mom, but she thinks it's too bland.''

''I think it's appropriate,'' he said.

Was that an opinion about Donald? Or was he merely speaking in generalities?

Greg's indifferent manner gave no clues. He reached over to lift the lid and peered inside. ''Carrot cake suits your vegetarian style.''

''Donald doesn't like carrot cake. The cream cheese frosting makes him gag.''

He nodded and pointed in the box. ''Is that a slice of lemon cake?''

''I think so. Why don't you have some? I'll get you a napkin, and you can eat it on your way to the warehouse.''

After she'd said the words, she worried that it may have seemed as if she was trying to get rid of him…which she was. But she didn't want to hurt his feelings.

Fortunately he seemed not to notice, rubbing his hands together and helping himself to a big piece of the lemony confection. ''That's okay. I'm in no rush.''

Then, pointing with the hunk of cake, he said,

"That repair job is not going to do you any good if the rest of the screen is rusting and falling apart. The old stuff won't support the added weight of the new. You ought to just replace the whole thing."

"Don't you start, too." Christina shook her head and went outside to push the needle back in. "I've already heard this lecture from Dad. Ever since I told him I plan to rip it all out eventually and put in a glass enclosure, he keeps reminding me about Donald wanting to move to Fair Oaks after we're married."

Christina started to come back in, but Greg brushed the crumbs from his hands and motioned for her to stay there while he took the needle on the inside.

"This is a terrific house," he said. "Why don't you two just live here?"

"Donald wants to move closer to town—and closer to his office." Unfortunately the idea of leaving this old home with its big rooms, tall ceilings and charming character to live in a cookie-cutter house that matched all the others in the regulated subdivision did not appeal to her. But she kept her opinion to herself. "I don't know. I'd like to keep the house and land so I can grow some flowers and shrubs to sell."

He rested his hand opposite hers where it touched the screen, and the pressure gave Christina an unexpected little rush.

"Sounds like a good plan. I'll bet you'd be a good businesswoman."

"My dad doesn't think so. He keeps telling me to forget about having my own greenhouse…that I have a great job at Plants Plus." He moved his hand, and she jabbed the needle through the screen. "Unfortunately my supervisor won't let me do the work I was hired for. Instead she keeps sending me on assignments the lawn maintenance crew is supposed to handle."

Greg nodded his sympathy, which encouraged her to continue.

"And my mom keeps telling me I have to just go along...put other people first." Christina paused as she pulled the white thread through both layers of mesh. The action raised a small brown cloud of rust dust. She didn't know why she was telling him all this, but now that she'd started it was hard to hold back. "And she backs it up by saying that people who only think of their own wishes eventually wind up in Daddy's jail."

Belatedly realizing what she'd said, Christina jerked her gaze up to Greg's eyes. Did he think she was referring to his supposed motive for taking her to the motel ten years ago?

His brown eyes seemed almost black as he held her gaze for a long moment. "So they do," he said and turned his attention to balancing the patch of new screen so that it was level.

"I'm sorry," she said. "I didn't mean that the way it sounded."

He gave her a forgiving smile, an expression as open as a fully bloomed cabbage rose. "So, what is it that *you* want?"

Christina sat back on her heels and gave a little laugh. "I love watching my plants grow, but lately that's not enough. I want children. Several of them. And I want to help them grow up healthy and happy.''

Greg paused a moment before quietly asking his next question. ''And you want Donald to give you those children?''

She could feel the smile on her face flatten into a straight line. Usually she didn't think of that aspect of their relationship. Not that Donald wasn't attractive in his own way. It was just something she pushed aside until she was ready to cross that bridge.

Greg's eyes narrowed, and she knew her hesitation had told him more than she'd intended.

''How did you and Donald meet?''

Glad to move the subject away from the personal details of her relationship with her fiancé, she tied off the thread and left the loose ends dangling from the screen.

''Dad met him through work, took a shine to him and eventually found an office for him downtown and started referring clients to him. After a while, he started thinking of Donald as a son, so he introduced us and—looky.'' She spread her arms wide. ''Now he's going to be a son-in-law.''

Greg nodded. ''Donald's a fine person.''

''You won't get any argument from me.'' So why wasn't she willing to give up everything and follow him wherever he led? Was she—as her mother suggested—selfishly putting her own wants ahead of those of her future husband?

Christina came back onto the porch and sagged into

the chair. Ten years ago she had followed Greg to the magistrate's office because it was what *he* wanted.

Currently her parents were still expecting her to do what they said, without an argument. After the wedding, Donald would probably take over the reins from her parents, steering her wherever his wishes led them.

Maybe it was the waning sun that made her feel so tired all of a sudden. Or maybe she was just tired of fighting to have a say in her own life…and always losing. But, whatever the reason, she now found herself looking forward to her wedding date as an old-time horse thief might look forward to the gallows.

Greg hovered over her, reached into the cake box and withdrew a slice of maple walnut. "One for the road," he said with a wink. "But before I go, I need to ask you a small favor."

She straightened in her chair. Whatever it was, the answer would have to be a firm and absolute *no*…because once he left here, there must be no more ties between them. "Look, I don't—"

"Before you say no, let me tell you it's right up your alley. It's just temporary work, and I'll pay you well."

"I already have a job. A full-time job." Lest he get other ideas, she added, "and my evenings are full."

He gave her a winsome smile meant to buckle her resolve, but Christina held firm. "Sorry."

After heaving a sigh of resignation, he raised one

dark eyebrow. "Fine," he said. "I'll just have to make other plans."

"Good idea." She walked with him to the flagstone path. Christina was proud of herself for not allowing him to coax her into doing what he wanted. It was best, she knew, that they sever all future contact.

Even so, a moment later she couldn't help feeling empty inside as she watched him drive out of her life forever.

The purple irises—six dozen pots of them—awaited Christina's arrival at work the next day. "Where did these come from?" she asked no one in particular as she reached for the shipping order taped to one of the pots.

The slip of paper showed her own name as the purchaser. And clear as day, under Items Ordered, it read Six Dozen Flats Of Purple Phlox.

She groaned. Now she would have to delay finishing the ground covering for the Tea Room's courtyard until this latest mix-up was straightened out.

No, she couldn't truthfully attribute this fiasco to an innocent mix-up. It was a blatant switch. Their supplier sometimes found himself with too much of one kind of plant on hand and not enough of another. When Christina had phoned in her order several days ago, he had told her another customer had canceled an order for irises and then he tried to get her to take them instead. And when she'd refused, he'd sent them anyway, apparently assuming she would just meekly accept them once they were in her hands.

She shoved the receipt into her slacks pocket and headed down the pebbled walkway toward her office at the far end of the greenhouse. Clenching her teeth, she vowed to burn up the phone lines today until this matter got settled according to *her* wishes. Christina Cline was no longer going to ''go along'' with whatever someone else wanted, just to make peace. It was time the world realized she had a right to make her own decisions.

The door to her office stood open, and Linda sat half perched on the edge of her desk. Good! Christina would start with her, insisting that her supervisor back her up when she demanded that the supplier make good on the order.

Linda laughed, a forced girlish sound coming from the woman who usually preferred to bark orders at her employees. ''Come on in,'' she said, inviting Christina into her own office. ''We've been waiting for you.''

We?

As she stepped into the office, she was aware of him before she even saw him. He seemed to fill the room with his presence, and when he stood to greet her, he overwhelmed her.

''Christina, I'd like you to meet Mr. Primo. He came here this morning to ask specifically for you. He wants you to work up some ideas for his new gym, and he's especially interested in floral dividers between the exercise stations.''

Apparently this was the "other plan" he'd made after she refused his offer yesterday.

Greg leaned forward, taking her hand in his with an utmost professional demeanor. "It's good to be doing business with you."

The only thing that broke his sincerity was the starburst of tiny lines at the outer edges of his eyes. Whenever he'd had that expression in high school, he'd been up to no good. And now Christina wanted no part of it. She'd learned her lesson about getting involved with Greg Primo. No matter how delectably intriguing he might be.

Withdrawing her hand as if she'd been exposed to aphids, she slid it into her slacks pocket. "I'm—I'm sorry, I can't work with you."

"Of course you can't," he said, grinning that devastating smile of his. "You'll do the plant stuff, and I'll do the gym stuff."

He knew exactly what she meant, but he was intentionally making this difficult for her. She swallowed and stood firm. "No, I mean I'm terribly busy." Turning to her supervisor, she said, "There's a problem with the Tea Room's ground cover order. It's going to set me back at least a couple of days."

"I can wait," Greg interjected.

If she hadn't known him better, she'd think he was wearing an expression of innocent cooperation.

Linda scooted off the desk and folded her arms over her chest. "You can handle the Tea Room and this, too." Then, tilting her head and widening her eyes in an unspoken message, she said significantly,

"This is the kind of assignment you told me you'd been waiting for."

Greg straightened and practically preened. "It is?"

"Not exactly," Christina said, not wishing to encourage him further. The sooner they severed all ties—including marriage bonds—the better it would be for everyone. "It wouldn't work out. I can't give you the kind of service you need."

"You'd be surprised." His voice was low and husky.

Linda's eyes widened again, this time in curiosity.

"What I mean is, my expertise is in outdoor landscape design. I believe you need an interior designer."

He rubbed a forefinger along his cheek, just below the fading scar that begged her to trace it with her lips. "And when it comes to the plants, the interior designer would subcontract that work to you. Am I right?"

She pressed a finger to her mouth, as if the action would still her wayward yearnings, and gave him a reluctant nod. "Yes, but we do different jobs. I don't know anything about wallpaper or lamps."

"Do you know anything about architecture?"

"Of course not. I'm a horticulturist."

"But that didn't keep you from giving me some excellent suggestions on the layout of the gym last week."

Linda looked from one to the other. "You two know each other?"

"In a manner of speaking." Christina moved away

from her unwelcome guest and pushed the door open in a not-so-subtle hint that his time here was up. It was enough that Donald had elected to take him on as a client—she had no desire to complicate matters further by allowing herself to get sucked back into his life. Or into his agendas. And especially into his arms. Not that she'd been invited…but the thought seemed to be present whenever he was around.

"Look, I don't know what's going on here," Linda said, breaking what was starting to stretch into an uncomfortable silence, "and I'm not sure I want to. Why don't I just leave you two to work things out between yourselves?"

Neither of them broke eye contact to acknowledge the other woman's departure.

Christina had just opened her mouth to tell him what she thought of him and his underhanded tactics when Linda popped back in. "Oh, and before you do anything rash," she told Christina, "just ask yourself whether you *really* want to spend the next couple of weeks operating the green machine."

And then she was gone. Christina knew her supervisor wasn't serious about putting her to work with the fertilizer crew, but her point was clear. Either Christina take this assignment, or there would be a price to pay.

She'd been railroaded again.

She curled her fists into tight balls and didn't relax them even when her fingernails bit into her palms.

"Oh, come on," Greg told her. "It can't be all that bad."

"I can only foresee problems coming from this," she said.

He closed the distance between them and took her hands in his, smoothing them flat with the pads of his fingers. She tried to pull away from his grasp, but he held her tightly.

"Why are you doing this? What do you want from me?"

He didn't answer her with words…just a look that said so much more than she wanted to know.

"It's not right," she said. "Can't you see what a bind you're putting me in?"

"I came to you because I want the best," he told her. "I won't settle for less."

Something told her he wasn't talking about her horticulture knowledge. She dared not consider the true intent behind his words.

"I've lived away from Morrison Heights for long enough." He continued massaging her fingers with his own. "I'm back to stay, and this time it's going to be as a pillar of the community…not as the town's troublemaker."

She felt her shoulders sag. He was back to stay. Back as a constant reminder of the foolish choice she'd made ten years ago.

"Where you live and what you do in the community have nothing to do with me."

He quirked his handsome mouth to one side before responding. "My dear, sweet Christina, you have no idea."

He gave her hands a final squeeze and released them as he stepped past her onto the pebbled pathway outside her door.

''You have absolutely no idea.''

CHAPTER FOUR

IT WAS at times like this that Christina wished she were self-employed. At least then she could choose the jobs she wanted and turn down those with former almost-lovers.

For three weeks, she'd stalled coming to the gym, using the time instead to take care of smaller, less urgent projects. When she could put it off no longer, she gathered up her notebook and measuring tape and drove down to the gym. The overcast skies echoed her sentiments exactly.

A new sign had been added since she'd been here last. Large metallic letters on the front of the warehouse spelled out The Body Shoppe. Inside, the changes were even more drastic. The place now looked more like an exercise center even though the equipment awaited assembly in one corner of the room.

Making herself at home, Christina picked her way around a ladder and several sealed cans of paint to the aerobics room where large mirrors were temporarily propped against the wall. She would start work here since it was the only room with no workmen.

"Oh, it's you," Greg said from behind her. "Trina said she thought the Jacuzzi guy came in here."

Christina wasn't prepared for the sight of him in

frayed denim shorts and a black T-shirt that hugged his chest and emphasized the contrast between the breadth of his shoulders and the narrowness of his waist. She gripped her clipboard and tried not to stare at the spectacular sight of such raw, masculine beauty.

"Um, Jacuzzi?" *Great, Christina,* she mentally chided, *impress him with your professionalism and brilliance.*

"Yeah, they're installing it now." He motioned back toward the pool area. "Why don't you come with me, and I'll show you what's been done since you were here last?"

Something warned her to say no, that it would be best to work at opposite ends of the building from him, but common sense kicked in and she accepted his offer. If she wanted to get this job over with as quickly as possible, it would be wise to get an overview of the building's new layout so she could move on to the creative stage of designing functional and attractive room barriers for him.

As they walked through the building, he brought her up to date on what had been accomplished since she'd last seen the place.

The new dressing room now had showers and lockers, the lounge was getting a juice bar and workers scurried like ants in every room.

"You must've hired magicians," she said, astounded at the miraculous improvements.

Greg shook his head, and a strand of dark hair fell to his forehead. He didn't bother to push it back in place. "Local businesses. I'm making it worth their while."

By now, they'd returned to the weight room, and the top few sheets on Christina's clipboard were filled with notes. "What's the big rush? Does it matter so much whether you open in a month or in six months?"

His dark eyes clouded over, and she suspected she'd touched a nerve. He called an instruction to a carpenter who was hammering a length of wood trim at the base of the wall. When a few seconds went by without a response, Christina assumed this question wouldn't get answered.

"The sooner the gym opens," he said at last, "the sooner the people of Morrison Heights can start erasing the memory of a no-good delinquent and start seeing me as a respectable businessman." He bent and picked up a soda can he'd left by the weight bench and took a long gulp, as if the action could make his past disappear along with the beverage. "When people mention my name," he said, looking directly at her, "I want them to say it with respect."

The intensity in his voice made Christina nervous. She gave a little laugh. "You sure don't sound like the same fellow who ran the principal's suit coat up the flag pole and insisted you didn't care what anyone thought of what you'd done."

He moved so he stood directly in front of her, his gaze gripping hers with a ferocity she'd never seen in him before.

"I'm not that same fellow anymore," he told her,

his voice deep and insistent. "And I want everyone in Morrison Heights to know that."

"You used to tell me that as long as you respected yourself, other people's opinions didn't concern you." What had made him buckle to the system he'd always jeered as a teen? "Why is the respect of strangers so important to you now?"

Greg crumpled the can and tossed it onto a pile of trash that was waiting to be swept up. "I have no desire to hide my past," he said honestly. "I just don't want to keep reliving it."

Something told Christina there was more… something more that he had chosen not to share.

Abruptly changing the subject, he added, "You have free rein to buy whatever supplies or equipment you think is appropriate for the gym. I trust your judgment."

Then he asked how long her various projects would take so he could start planning for the grand opening.

Of course. That was it. He must be concerned that his hell-raiser reputation would be bad for business. No wonder he'd insisted on opening the gym in what was turning into a trendy, upscale neighborhood. Obviously that was part of the new image he wanted to project.

Two plumbers walked between them, carrying lengths of pipe, and headed toward the showers. Then an electrician called out to Greg to ask where he wanted the ceiling fans to go.

Christina could see she wouldn't get much accom-

plished amid all this confusion. "I think I'll go outside and see about that jogging trail you suggested."

By the end of the day, she was ready to scream.
The overcast skies had kept their promise and delivered a fine drizzle all day, forcing her inside where
she couldn't turn around without bumping into a
tradesman or, worse, Greg. And each time she saw
him, she was reminded that he was the one who had
called the shots to have her working for him. Well, it
wouldn't be long before her ties to him would be
severed and she'd be able to regain control of her life.

Meanwhile, she couldn't get away from him.
Eventually, after taking measurements throughout the
rest of the building, she retreated to the half-finished
office where Trina sat typing a grand-opening flyer
on the computer. In front of Trina's desk was a gaping
hole in the wall that would soon be covered with a
pane of glass.

"Just look at him," the blonde said, pointing toward the weight room where Greg helped lift a water
cooler and set it by the wall. "Have you ever seen
such a human dynamo?" She winked, and the cheek-
sweeping lashes hovering above her eye dipped a salute. "His legs aren't bad, either."

Christina had already noticed but had tried not to
focus on his incredible attributes.

"And those muscles," Trina continued. "I tell you,
I wouldn't be here right now if he'd been a scrawny
little guy. He saved me from certain disaster the night
he offered me this job."

She was clearly launching into another Greg-is-a-saint speech, and Christina knew there would be no stopping her once she'd started.

But that wouldn't keep her from trying. "It's five o'clock. Time to pack up and go home."

"Oh, I won't be leaving until Greg goes home. I owe him so much. It's the least I can do to stay late in case he needs any letters typed or errands run."

"That's an awful lot of loyalty for his having offered you a job."

"Hon, he saved my *life!*" Trina swiveled in her chair to face her. "That man—that saint—rescued me from a bunch of rowdy drunks at a little honky-tonk where I was performing. That's how he got that scar under his eye."

She should have known he'd earned the scar while coming to someone else's defense. Her thoughts veered back to Trina's other comment.

"You sang?"

"Of course I sang. What else did you think I'd be doing there?"

Christina decided to let that one go. "Back in high school, Greg was always sticking up for other people, even if it meant getting into trouble himself."

Despite his rebellious ways, he'd always been very *other* oriented, selflessly putting the concerns of others before his own. Knowing that about him, she'd been surprised by his pronouncement that he was now turning his attention toward cleaning up his reputation.

Not that there was anything wrong with that, but it just didn't seem to click.

Christina gathered up her belongings, said good-night to Trina and made her way past the recently delivered stacks of chairs that would go into the meeting room at the back of the building.

Giving Greg a little wave, she started out the new double doors. Then, remembering the annulment papers that she'd been carrying around in her purse for the past couple of weeks, she went back in.

"Forget something?" Greg smiled, the action causing a small dimple to form in his cheek and a knot of desire to form in her heart.

"Almost." Christina took the papers out as she met him in the middle of the room. She unstacked one of the chairs and handed him the papers and her clipboard. "You need to sign this."

He didn't sit. Nor did he take the papers from her.

"I lived up to my end of the bargain," she reminded him, pushing the clipboard closer to him.

"Yes, and I'll live up to mine," he promised, "but we'll need to hold off another week on that."

"Another week? You signed the lease two weeks ago. There's no reason to delay this any longer."

"I did sign the lease," he said, pulling out a second chair and sinking into it. Christina refused his invitation to take the other one. "Mrs. Odell's lawyer is supposed to be sending me a copy soon but, until I have it in hand, I'd rather not risk jeopardizing the deal."

Christina clenched her teeth, annoyed that he was finding yet another excuse to delay the annulment. A hiccup lodged in her throat and she swallowed hard, hoping to suppress the evidence of stress.

"Instead you're jeopardizing my wedding plans," she said evenly.

"I promise you, I'll sign the papers in plenty of time before the wedding. Just bear with me a little longer."

The one thing she wanted most in her life—control over her own affairs—was being denied her in so many ways today. First, she had to show up at this job even though her first preference would be to keep as many miles between her and Greg as possible, and now he was forcing her to wait for papers that would ultimately determine whether she could carry through with her plans to marry Donald.

And, to top matters off, even her diet had been controlled by the fact that the nearby restaurants had no vegetarian choices on their menus. At least the stray dog had been happy when she'd given him the meat patty from her deluxe hamburger.

She hiccuped out loud this time. Greg met her eyes, and she knew he was aware that he had caused her hiccups. And she hated that he even had control over that!

The frustration overwhelmed her, and Christina felt that if she stayed a minute longer she would blow up. And then Greg *surely* would know how deeply he affected her. She refused to give him that satisfaction.

Lifting the chair that he had left vacant for her, she returned it to the stack with a thump. And before he could rise to his feet, she pushed past the small tower of chairs to leave before another hiccup escaped.

She heard him get up, and as she pushed open the broad double door she heard a crash and a yell.

Christina turned around in time to see Greg rising from amid the pile of chairs that had apparently toppled in his path.

"I think I broke something," he said, cradling his right arm.

Immediately, the storm that had been brewing inside Christina evaporated in the face of her concern for Greg. Picking her way past the upended chairs, she went to his side.

He grimaced briefly as he lifted the T-shirt sleeve to examine his upper arm. For the space of an instant, Christina wondered if he was faking the injury to gain sympathy after having angered her with his refusal to sign the annulment papers.

But, no, one look at the pained lines around his eyes told her it was real. And if they hadn't, the red mark and swelling on his arm were enough to convince her.

Now the guilt kicked in full force. "I'm so sorry," she said, wanting to soothe the pain away, but not daring to touch his bared arm.

"You shouldn't be sorry. It was my clumsiness that caused it."

"No, that's not true." She started to argue that if she hadn't pushed past the chairs in her anger, they wouldn't have been shoved off balance. But that would just be wasting valuable time while his arm puffed up even more.

"Greggie, are you all right?" Wobbling on her stiletto heels, Trina's balance seemed even more precarious than the chairs had been.

"Yeah, I'm fine," he insisted. "I'll just get a little ice and—"

"And he'll hold it on his arm while I take him to the emergency room," Christina finished for him.

"I'll take him," Trina volunteered. "My car's right outside."

"No, it was all my fault—I'll drive him."

He tried to resist, saying some ice and a little rest was all he needed. But Christina held firm, asking Trina to lock up the gym after the workmen left.

Later, in the hospital waiting room, Greg handed her the plastic bag of ice that Trina had prepared for him. "I'm getting tired of holding this. Do you mind?"

Once again, Christina studied his face for clues that his words held an ulterior motive. But he merely closed his eyes and sagged back against the ripped vinyl cushion.

In that position, he looked so sweet…so vulnerable…that she found herself wanting to take him in her arms and cradle his head to her chest while she willed his pain away.

Guilt stung her conscience. She had behaved badly after he'd asked her to wait yet again on getting the papers signed. He had every right to be angry with her for causing the accident, but he had tried to assure her it was his own fault for not being more careful. That wasn't true, of course. With his strength and highly developed coordination, he could have easily caught his fall if it had been merely a case of momentary carelessness.

Christina touched the ice bag to his arm, and guilt squeezed her heart when he winced in response. "I'm sorry," she said for what must have been the tenth time since his fall.

Greg opened his eyes. Not bothering to turn his head, he followed her with his gaze. "When you go into nurture mode, you really go all out." He studied her face for a moment and said softly, "It's nice."

She wasn't quite sure whether he was referring to her mothering or what he saw when he looked at her. Considering the former a safer level of conversation, she gave him a teasing grin. "If you'd been a little more considerate and burned yourself instead, I could have done a better job of nurturing. There's enough aloe in my purse to cover half the population of Morrison Heights."

He smiled, and she was warmed by the tenderness of his expression. Her thoughts raced back to the way he had been in high school. Brash, and so very confident, he seemed to have everything that she had wanted for herself.

A people pleaser, Christina had worked hard to do what was right, and she enjoyed the accolades and compliments bestowed on her for her efforts. It felt good to be thought of so highly, but with that good favor came expectations. High expectations that she continue to conform to the will of others…her father, teachers, her friends and society in general.

Greg, on the other hand, had a freedom she'd never known. Because people held no such expectations for him, he was free to do as he wished. And it seemed as though he always had more fun than anyone she knew. Sure, that fun came with a price, but sometimes she found herself wishing she'd been able and willing to pay that price. Even now.

Especially now.

Her father would have had a conniption if he'd known she wanted to be more like the boy who represented the very elements he was trying to eliminate in their town.

And now he was back. And, once again, he was creating chaos in her life.

"You're mighty quiet," he said, laying a hand over her fingers where she touched his arm. "Is something wrong?"

Christina drew in a breath and considered the man who had the ability to send her emotions skittering from anger to concern to…to something else that she wasn't willing to examine.

A slight scowl touched his features as he seemed to appraise her. "Or are you just missing Donald?"

Donald. She'd forgotten all about him! "Oh my gosh," she said, rummaging in her purse for some coins to put in the pay phone. "He's probably wondering where I am."

Taking the purse from her to still her frantic search, Greg felt a smile creep across his face. So she *hadn't* thought about her fiancé while she'd been with him. Perhaps, as he'd hoped, there was less to that relationship than met the eye.

''Don't worry,'' he said. ''Trina will tell him where you are.''

She relaxed back into the chair. ''That's right. He was supposed to pick up your ledgers after work today. I'm sure Trina will fill him in on what happened.''

This time Greg's smile stretched across his face. If their relationship was all it was cracked up to be, she wouldn't be satisfied with letting another woman relay messages to her fiancé. She'd be on that phone, talking to Donald herself.

Come to think of it, if things were as they should be, she would have taken Trina up on her offer to drive him here in the first place. And that bit of knowledge led him to the gratifying conclusion that Christina still had feelings for him. If he played his cards right, perhaps he could show her that those feelings were love.

But he'd have to work fast if he was to accomplish his mission before the wedding. With only a little more than three weeks to go, he'd have to stick by her every possible minute, reminding her with his actions and his presence, of what they used to have. Of what they *could* have had. And of what they still could have.

A woman in scrub clothes stepped into the waiting room and read from the chart in her hands. ''Mr. Primo?''

Greg quickly rose to his feet and offered his left hand to Christina. "I'm still here," he told the woman.

He was still here, all right, and he wasn't about to give Christina up without a fight.

The next three days saw tremendous changes in the gym as workers put in long hours to get the place ready for the grand opening. Although his right arm wasn't broken, it was still too sore to use much. But he found he could wield a paint roller effectively with his left hand.

The best part about this particular job was that it put him in the same room with Christina. More than once, he realized he'd stopped painting to watch her work. And just as often, he'd been pleased to catch her looking in his direction.

This time, however, she seemed not to notice his perusal as she climbed up on a stationary bike and slowly worked the pedals. Her attention was fixed on the knee-high room dividers that would soon serve double duty as plant holders and benches for sitting. She was obviously checking to see how much foliage she'd need to create a good privacy barrier. He couldn't help admiring the way her chinos embraced her legs in their smooth, leisurely pumping motion. Her white top had worked its way out of her waist-band to show a glimpse of bare, tanned skin.

Christina turned and once again caught him watching her. Rather than seem like a love-struck schoolboy, he broke their eye contact and set the roller brush in the paint tray.

"Is your arm still hurting?" she asked.

"A little." He stretched, spreading both arms wide to relax the kinks in his aching muscles, and was pleased to see Christina's gaze drop to his chest. Apparently he wasn't the only one enjoying the view across the room. "I think I'll follow the doctor's advice and get in the hot tub for a while. Want to join me?" When she hesitated, he added, "You could probably use a good soak after doing all that lifting today."

He'd tried to make the words sound casual, as if it didn't matter whether she accompanied him or not, but Christina's sudden halt on the bike had him wondering if his motives were more apparent than he'd thought. Did she know how much he wanted to see her nearly naked and wet?

"Thanks, but I, um…I have a lot of stuff to do tonight."

"Oh," Greg said, allowing his disappointment to show in his voice. "Then I'll just have to do the therapy exercises by myself."

He waited, almost certain she wouldn't be able to refuse if it involved nurturing.

After a couple of silent seconds, she started to waver, just as he'd expected. "I don't have a swimsuit."

Greg was tempted to suggest she do without one, but he knew that wouldn't go over very well with her. So he settled for the next best thing. "Trina tried out the hot tub the day it was installed. Maybe her suit is still here somewhere. I'm sure she wouldn't mind if you borrowed it.''

Christina paused and seemed to be carefully considering the invitation. ''How long are you supposed to do your exercises?''

Apparently she was experiencing a stab of guilt. Greg certainly didn't blame her for the accident, but if it helped swing her decision to the positive, then he wouldn't argue the point.

''About thirty minutes.''

She gave him a hesitant smile. ''I suppose a nice, hot soak would feel good about now.''

It was all Greg could do to keep from punching the air with a victory fist. Instead he helped her find the swimsuit and said he'd meet her in the hot tub.

Most of the workmen were gone for the day, and Trina had gone shopping for decorative prints to hang in her office. As for Donald, he had called to say he'd be working late tonight and that he would see Christina tomorrow when he came to work on the gym's books. So her excuse that she had a lot to do this evening was nothing more than that…an excuse.

When, after a long delay, she came into the pool room, Greg couldn't keep his eyes off her. He tried not to stare as she eased herself into the tub, tugging self-consciously at the straps she'd tightened with safety pins to take up the excess length. The black one-piece suit fit snugly across her generous hips. The top, which had been skimpy on Trina, who was both taller and fuller-figured, hung loosely on Christina's smaller frame.

Her quiet shyness brought to mind their interrupted time at the motel. He wondered if she found the intimacy of being alone with him in such close quarters—not to mention without most of their clothes—disconcerting. To put her at ease, he handed her the instructions the doctor had given him and asked her to help him with the exercises.

She seemed relieved to have something to do, and in a few moments they were laughing and talking as if they were working together on a class assignment.

Greg loved the gentle touch of her small hands on his shoulder as she helped him work the stiffness out of the strained muscle. And he enjoyed her playful shove that sent him under for a thorough soaking after he told her the joke about how many vegetarians it takes to change a lightbulb. But as much as he enjoyed her company, he wanted more. He wanted Christina. He wanted her love.

And then he had to go and ruin their fun by mentioning Donald's name. "So what's with you two?" he said, wanting to know exactly where she stood in that relationship. "Why are you with Donald?"

GET A FREE TEDDY BEAR...

You'll love this adorable bean-filled teddy bear. This wonderfully soft bear has beautiful brown eyes and wears a cheery chequered bow around his neck. Measuring just over 6" he is sure to delight everyone who sees him. And he's yours FREE when you accept this no-risk offer!

AND FOUR FREE BOOKS!

Here's the chance to get four Mills & Boon® novels from the Enchanted™ series **absolutely free!** These books have a retail value of at least £2.30

There's no catch. You're under no obligation to buy anything. We charge nothing - ZERO - for your first shipment. And you don't have to make any minimum number of purchases - not even one!

Find out for yourself why thousands of readers enjoy receiving books by post from the Reader Service™. They like the convenience of home delivery... they like getting the best new novels before they are available in the shops... and they love the fact that **postage and packing is entirely free!** Why not try us and see! Return this card promptly. You don't even need a stamp!

YES! Please send me four free Enchanted™ novels and my free Teddy Bear. I understand that I am under no obligation to purchase any books, as explained overleaf. I am over 18 years of age.

N9II

MS/MRS/MISS/MR   INITIALS
                                                    BLOCK CAPITALS PLEASE
SURNAME

ADDRESS

                              POSTCODE

◄ DETACH AND RETURN THIS CARD TODAY. NO STAMP NEEDED! ►

NO OBLIGATION TO BUY!

THE READER SERVICE™ : HERE'S HOW IT WORKS

Accepting the free books and gift places you under no obligation to buy anything. You may keep the books and gift and return the despatch note marked 'cancel'. If we do not hear from you, about a month later we will send you 6 more books and invoice you just £2.40 each*. That's the complete price - there is no extra charge for postage and packing. You may cancel at any time, otherwise every month we'll send you 6 more books, which you may either purchase or return - the choice is yours.

*Terms and prices subject to change without notice.

NO STAMP NEEDED!

THE READER SERVICE™
FREEPOST CN81
CROYDON
SURREY
CR9 3WZ

NO STAMP NEEDED IF POSTED IN THE U.K. OR N.I.

YOURS FREE!

CHAPTER FIVE

CHRISTINA pushed the wet hair out of her face and grew serious. This was the second time she'd completely forgotten about Donald while she was with Greg. She was a woman who took her commitments seriously, and it bothered her that her fiancé could be wiped so easily from her mind. "I don't know what you mean," she hedged.

Leaning back to let the water jets surge around him, he said simply, "Well, you two don't act like a couple who are soon to be married."

Turning her back to Greg, she reached for a towel to dry her face. How could she respond to a statement like that? It was true they didn't fawn all over each other like a couple of giggly teenagers, but was that reason enough to question their commitment?

"Do you love him?"

Did she love him? She'd asked herself that question a thousand times, and she still didn't know the answer for certain. Theirs was a special relationship, one built on honor and respect and mutual admiration. Christina felt certain that in time, after they'd had a chance to live together and come to know each other on more personal terms, her feelings would mature and transform into a deeper kind of affection.

"I don't know why you're asking me this."

"Are you evading the question?"

"No. Of course I love him." Right now it was the kind of love one human feels for another. As one *friend* feels for another. Someday, after it had a chance to grow, hers would be the kind of love a wife harbors for her husband. "Donald is a kind and decent person."

"So are at least half the men in this town, but I don't see you planning to marry them." He flashed her a grin, but it did little to lighten the mood in the room.

"What are you getting at?"

"I want you to be happy, Christina."

"I *am* happy." She moved away from him, the nearness suddenly making her uncomfortable, and sat opposite him. "And I will be happy after we're married and have a few children."

He made no move to close the distance between them, but it seemed as though he was sitting right beside her. When he spoke, his voice was soft and husky. "I could give you children."

She stood abruptly, clutching the swimsuit top to keep from leaving it behind. "I don't think we should be talking about this."

Christina tried to ignore him as he watched her dry off, but a rabbit could just as easily ignore a wolf preparing to pounce on it.

"How about tomorrow after work?" he asked as if he hadn't been the least bit out of line. "Will you help me with my exercises again?"

She wrapped the towel around herself and knotted

it between her breasts. "I can't. I'm fixing a practice dinner for Donald's parents tomorrow."

"A practice dinner?"

Why hadn't she just said she was having Donald over for dinner? Now she had captured Greg's attention, and he wouldn't leave her alone until his curiosity was satisfied.

"Donald and I thought it would be a good idea to meet with his parents on casual terms before the wedding…you know, discuss final preparations and hopefully get to know each other a little better." Feeling a little silly for being so nervous about spending time with the Winklers, she combed her fingers through her wet hair. But Donald had insisted her nervousness was justified, considering the problems his mother had created prior to his older brother's marriage. "And since meat loaf is their favorite meal, I wanted to make sure I get the recipe just right."

"Meat loaf, huh? I never thought I'd see the day." He chuckled.

"Actually, Donald said I should just be myself and fix what I normally cook—"

"Smart man."

"—so I decided to compromise with a vegetarian meat loaf. I just hope they'll like it."

"Want me to taste-test it for you? I don't mind being a guinea pig."

"That's sweet of you, but Donald is already planning to take care of that."

"But he won't be as brutally honest as I will."

Greg was probably right on that account. Donald

was so easygoing that she doubted he'd tell her even if he didn't like what she prepared.

"Besides," Greg continued, "it would be no inconvenience on my part. I've just been having sandwiches the last couple of nights since it's kind of hard to maneuver around the kitchen with this bum shoulder." He straightened his arm stiffly to prove his point.

At that, Christina felt like the lowest kind of worm. She'd turned down his offer because she thought he was just being kind, and yet he was really longing for a hot meal. A man the size of Greg, who did as much physical work as he performed each day, needed something more filling than just a sandwich for dinner.

"Now that you mention it, Donald doesn't care much for vegetarian cooking, but he always compliments me on the meals I prepare." She tried not to stare as he got out of the hot tub and rubbed the towel over his body. "It would help to have an unbiased opinion."

He smiled as if he'd just scored the winning touchdown at a football game.

She knew Donald wouldn't mind her spontaneous invitation. It seemed he couldn't say enough good things about his new client, so she knew he would enjoy Greg's company.

For her, however, it would be an interesting test...and not only of her cooking skills.

Christina hoped her meat loaf wouldn't be as much of a disaster as the rest of the day had been. First, the stone company had delivered a too-coarse gravel for the jogging trail. Then, while she was setting a fern near the Jacuzzi, her engagement ring had slipped off her finger and rolled into the water. After Greg helped her fish it out with a net, she'd been afraid of risking another such incident and had put the diamond ring deep in her pants pocket where it would be safe. And she had feared that, by not wearing the symbol of her commitment, she had hurt Donald's feelings when he arrived later to work on the books. Strangely enough, his reaction had been less of hurt or anger than mere curiosity—even before she'd explained the situation to him.

To make an odd situation even odder, she couldn't help noticing that Donald seemed to be acting rather peculiar lately, especially whenever Trina was around.

And now, on top of everything else, Greg was "helpfully" offering advice on everything from her furniture arrangement to how she could best hide the unattractively patched hole in the porch screen.

"What about this sunflower picture?" he asked as she pulled the meat loaf out of the oven. "Want me to put it in your spare bedroom?"

"No, of course not. My mother would think I didn't like it if I took it down. That was her first attempt at watercolors in her Late Starters art class."

"You're telling me."

She would have bristled at the verbal dig, but when he took the glass dish from her to put it on the dining-room table, she saw that he was grinning. Funny how his shoulder didn't seem to be bothering him tonight.

"That's so like you," he said. "Putting something that ugly on display so as not to hurt the giver's feelings."

She hadn't really thought about it, but she supposed he was right.

Returning to the kitchen, he pointed at her ear. "Like those earrings. Did your mom make them, too?"

Christina touched a finger to one of the orange beaded creations that dangled from her lobe. "No, Donald's eight-year-old niece made them for me."

He shook his head. "Just be yourself. If people don't already love you for who you are, then they're not worth the effort."

It was such a little thing, and if it made people happy, then it pleased her as well. Besides, she didn't want to run the risk of alienating Donald's mother. Christina had heard the horror stories about how she'd made things so difficult for her older son and his fiancée that the couple ultimately ditched their plans for a large wedding and eloped instead. Mrs. Winkler eventually accepted her daughter-in-law, but Christina didn't want to risk the older woman's displeasure.

She reached into the cabinet for three plates. "I wonder what happened to Donald. He should have been here by now."

Greg took the plates from her and returned one to the shelf. "He said to tell you he'll be working late at the gym and that you and I should go on without him.''

Go on without him? But this dinner was for *his* parents. ''He's the one who suggested I have this practice run. What could he be doing that's more important than this?''

The sheepish expression Greg wore gave her a clue that he was somehow involved.

''I told him Mrs. Odell's lawyer was dragging his feet on getting me a notarized copy of the lease, so he thought it would be best to stay and draft a letter.''

Her first thought, based on his guilty reaction, was that he did it on purpose. He knew Donald's compulsion for staying at work each day until everything on his to-do list was completed.

She thought back to Greg's comment that he could give her the children she wanted. Had he seen this as an opportunity to rekindle something between them if only they had some time alone together?

''Considering how anxious you are to finalize the annulment and get on with the wedding,'' he added, ''I thought he'd want to put that at the top of his list for tomorrow.'' Greg shrugged. ''But he said since Trina was available to type the letter for him, he'd get it over with now and hand-deliver it tonight.''

Feeling foolish for having suspected Greg of being underhanded, she avoided his eyes as she emptied the squash from the steamer into a serving dish. Of course he wasn't thinking of her in that way. His comment must have been merely a passing flirtation. The Italian Rapscallion was known for his charm and for his ability to make women's hearts flutter. So why should she think she was being treated any differently?

"Thank you," she said, moving past him to place the dish on the dining-room table. "I suppose that is best."

So why did she feel so disappointed? Was it because of Greg's apparent eagerness to sever their marriage?

Christina gave herself a mental shake. Of course it wasn't. Most likely, her disappointment sprang from Donald's absence tonight and the knowledge that he'd be spending the evening with Trina instead of here where he belonged.

"Anything to help an old friend." Greg slid into the chair opposite her and started helping himself to the overabundant mounds of food she'd prepared. "Hey, homemade bread! You're a real Suzy Homemaker."

"Maybe you should taste it before you make any decisions about my cooking." She spooned some mashed potatoes onto her plate. "I just hope Donald's parents approve. Especially Mrs. Winkler. She seems so proper, and I think she worries that I'm not good enough for her son."

In midbite, Greg sputtered and started coughing.

"Are you all right?" She started to go to him, but he waved her back into her chair.

His eyes were watering, and he gave her the okay sign as he took a sip from his glass. "The question should be," he said, after catching his breath, "is Donald good enough for *you?*"

"That's very sweet of you, but I understand his mother's protectiveness since he's the baby of the family." Christina cut a thick slice of bread and buttered it. "His mother is very much in favor of the marriage, but I don't want to give her any cause for doubt."

"Then why don't we rehearse?" Greg sat up straight in his chair, pursed his lips and held his fork with pinky finger extended. "I'll be Mrs. Winkler."

Christina laughed. "I said she's proper, not stuffy."

Ignoring her comment, he continued the charade. When he spoke, his voice was high and squeaky. "Do tell me, my dear, what is it about my boy that attracts you most? Is it his money, his good looks, or his scintillating conversation?"

She laughed again, only the humor was less in how he said it than what he said. "Donald's law practice is so new that it'll be a while before he's well into the black. But I have confidence that he'll be very successful someday."

As for his looks, he was clean and well-groomed. He was no Mel Gibson, but neither was he a ghoul. And their conversations were centered mostly around their jobs and Donald's local political aspirations. He wanted to be mayor someday, and she had no doubt he would achieve his goal.

But there was no need to raise Greg's eyebrows by mentioning her thoughts on the latter two subjects. Although their relationship might seem bland to an outsider, it suited them just fine.

Rather than press for an answer to the rest of his question, Greg moved on to a different topic. "You're a lovely girl," he continued in the voice that was meant to mimic an elderly society matron, "and you're from a good family. Why is it you haven't married before now?"

She really didn't want to rehash this with Greg, and she didn't know why he would try to bring up their old relationship. Christina ate a bite of her zucchini before responding. "Why don't you try the veggie meat loaf and tell me what you think?"

Dropping the fake voice, Greg met her eyes across the table and held her gaze. "It's a reasonable thing that any mother might want to know about her future daughter-in-law. What will you tell her if she asks you this next week?" His next words were carefully measured. "That you hadn't found anyone you loved before now?"

Christina paused, not wanting to hurt his feelings. "I suppose I could say something like that. After all, you and I were just a couple of kids. We didn't know what we were doing."

"I knew what I was doing."

She supposed he did. Greg Primo had always been the kind of man who played to win, and he'd been determined to win her that spring day ten years ago. When his move was thwarted, the game was apparently over as far as he was concerned. Checkmate.

Christina swallowed but said nothing. She had no idea what she would say if such a situation arose.

"Are you going to tell them you've been married before?"

She nodded. "I won't keep it a secret. What about you?" she asked. "Why haven't you remarried?"

She expected him to say he'd been too busy establishing his exercise gyms to get involved with a woman. Instead he repeated what he'd told her the night he returned to her life.

"I won't settle for less than the best," he said evenly. "When I buy equipment for the gyms, I make sure it's of top quality. And once I find what I want, I intend to keep it a long time."

The painful memory of him sending her away after his arrest pricked at her like a burr in her sock. She had intended for theirs to be a forever kind of marriage, and she'd been prepared to honor their vows to the fullest. It had been Greg who decided she wasn't worth keeping…that she wasn't top quality.

Would Donald have similar concerns after a few years of marriage to her? Would he decide that, in accepting a relationship with no spark or sizzle, he was settling for less than the best? And if he did, where would she be then?

Greg returned to their earlier conversation, refusing to let it drop. "I suppose you'll tell the Winklers that you've waited all your life for someone like Donald, and all your dreams are coming true now that you're marrying Mr. Right."

"Oh good grief, you make it sound like we're madly in—" Christina stopped herself, horrified at what she'd almost revealed.

What she *had* revealed. Greg's intense concentration told her he knew exactly what she'd been about to say.

''You once told me you believed in happily-ever-after,'' he said quietly. ''How can you be happy, married to a man you don't love?''

''I do love him. He's good and kind and decent—''

''But you don't love him the way a woman is supposed to love a man.''

''Not all marriages are built on that type of love,'' she insisted. ''I can be very content with Donald. And contentment is a form of happiness.''

''So you're willing to settle for less than the best?''

Christina took the napkin from her lap and laid it on the table. ''I'm not going to sit here while you disparage my fiancé and put ideas—I mean words— into my mouth.''

''You're right, I was out of line,'' Greg said, raising his hands in surrender. ''Let's switch to a safer topic.''

Christina relaxed back into her chair, prepared to finish her dinner now that he was agreeing to behave more like a gentleman.

In his old-lady voice, he prompted, ''Tell me about your job. Do you plan to stay at Plants Plus after the children start coming?''

She eyed him warily, wondering if he was taking a back-door approach to probing in her personal life.

He lifted his shoulders. ''As your future mother-in-law, I need to know these things.''

What could it hurt? Besides, it was a subject in

which the Winklers would likely be interested. She may as well rehearse it now.

"I'm hoping that by the time the first child is on the way, I'll have my own landscape design company up and running."

She paused, waiting for the inevitable words of warning about the hazards of self-employment. To her surprise, he was very encouraging.

"You'd do well on your own. I can see you working hard to give your clients what they want." He dug into his meat loaf. "Too hard, maybe. Hey, this is good."

"What do you mean by that?"

"I mean it cuts like meat loaf and tastes like meat loaf. If I didn't know better, I'd think it was the real thing." He took another forkful, dipped it in the tomato sauce it had been baked in and popped it into his mouth, chewing with genuine enthusiasm.

Christina was relieved to know that her culinary experiment was a success, but his previous statement had piqued her curiosity. "Thanks, but I was referring to what you said about me working too hard."

"Oh, that." He wiped the napkin across his mouth, and Christina's gaze followed his gesture. "I meant you try so hard to please others that sometimes you lose sight of what you want for yourself. I'd hate for you to make yourself miserable by trying to make everyone else happy." He reached across the table. "Mind if I have seconds?"

"Help yourself."

She leaned back in her chair and watched him eat.

He attacked it the way he approached everything else in life…with forceful enthusiasm. "So what's so wrong with wanting to please others? It gives me pleasure to watch you enjoy the meal I prepared. And it would give me pleasure to design a lawn that satisfies my client. Isn't that what happiness is all about…finding pleasure wherever you can?"

"Yes, as long as it's your own pleasure you're experiencing and not just a by-product of some else's." Finished, he pushed his plate away. "Tell me something…do Donald's parents want you to marry him? And is it what your parents want?"

"Of course. My parents like Donald, and his parents seem to like me."

Greg got up and walked around to her. Extending a hand to her as she rose from the table, he persisted in his line of questioning. "Answer me honestly. Do you want to marry Donald as much as they want you to marry him?"

Christina felt her face grow warm. Jerking her hand away from his grasp, she busied herself with clearing the table. "Of course I want to marry him. Why would you ask such a thing?"

Greg gathered up some of the dishes and followed her into the kitchen. "Because you're still married to me. After all these years, you've never made a move to get a divorce. And, knowing you the way I do, I'd venture a guess that you're still a virgin."

"I really don't think that's any of your business!" The dishes clattered into the sink. It would be his fault if any of them were broken.

"Ah, but it's true, isn't it? Because you're not the kind of woman who would cheat on her husband, no matter how long he's been gone."

She glared at him, angry that he was making much more out of this than it deserved. "For your information, I take my promises—my vows—very seriously. Even if it is only a paper marriage."

"Those vows also said 'until death do us part,'" he reminded her.

"Death of a partner, death of a marriage, what's the difference?" She turned on her heel and went back into the dining room. When she returned a moment later with the place mats, he was leaning against the sink, waiting for her. And a smug grin covered his face.

"A marriage isn't dead until the last bit of love is gone." He watched as she shook the crumbs from the place mats into the sink and rinsed them down the drain. He moved closer and took her in his arms.

Christina started to pull away, but his next words stilled her.

"Last time I checked, it was alive and breathing."

She stood as if frozen, aware of his chin resting against the top of her head. Aware of an intense desire to melt into his embrace and kiss him with all the frustrated longing that had been building up for ten years. Aware that, by not moving away, she was inviting him to continue holding her. And yet, still, she didn't move away.

"It's alive for you, isn't it?"

It was, indeed, alive. No matter how hard she'd

tried to smother her feelings, they always managed to resurface. But it would be madness to admit as much to him.

Come to think of it, he hadn't made any confessions of his own. For all she knew, he'd been talking about *her* love. Otherwise, he would have said "it's alive for you, *too*."

Did he have a motive for wanting to keep her dangling on a string? Once the lease was delivered from Mrs. Odell's lawyer, Christina would be delivered from any further obligation to Greg. Unless, of course, there was something he hadn't told her. He was a man who would do whatever it took to get what he wanted. She hadn't thought he was a man who would manipulate a person who had once cared about him. But she hadn't thought he would play on her fanciful dreams of a fairy-tale wedding to get her to go to bed with him, either.

With great restraint, she stepped out of the mesmerizing circle of his arms and sought to clear the fog from her head. Reverting to the reason she'd invited him here in the first place, she took his hand and shook it warmly.

"Thank you, Mrs. Winkler, for joining us for dinner tonight. I hope that next time we get together, Donald will be here with us. I'll even try on the wedding dress you lent me."

A sense of self-preservation had prompted her to add that last comment. It wouldn't hurt to remind him that she was engaged to be married, and that she was going through with it, no matter how much he confused her with his talk of lingering love.

Greg hesitated only a moment before taking the cue and returning her handshake. Lapsing into the high-pitched tone, he said, "Dinner was lovely, my dear." Then, in his own voice, he added, "I'd really like to get that meat loaf recipe."

"Sure. I'm glad you liked it."

As she walked him to the door, she felt more confident about cooking dinner for the Winklers. Unfortunately Greg had managed to raise doubts about her relationship with Donald that she'd previously been so successful at suppressing.

CHAPTER SIX

IT SEEMED as though she had just fallen asleep when the doorbell rang. Prying one eyelid open, she squinted at the bedside clock. Six-thirty, a half hour before her alarm was set to go off. Although it was Saturday, she was scheduled to work overtime at the gym today.

"Who could be here at this time of morning?"

Then, fearing there might be some tragedy, she hurled herself out of bed and ran to the door, not even taking time to grab her robe. Peeking out the lowest of the three panes of glass in the door, she saw Greg staring back at her.

His hair sticking up on one side and his face unshaved, he looked as though he hadn't slept any better than she had. But that didn't keep him from giving her the once-over when she opened the door to him.

"Is something wrong?"

"Yeah, I think my wallet fell out of my pocket when I was here last night. Mind if I take a look?"

She sighed and let him in. She was thankful that no catastrophic emergency prompted the unscheduled visit, but she sure wished she could have slept those extra thirty minutes. "If you had called, I could have brought it to you at the gym."

"Nice pajamas," he said, taking in her mismatched

114

baggy shorts and oversize T-shirt. "I couldn't have waited that long. I have a killer headache, and the aspirin is in my wallet."

He made himself at home, lifting cushions on the sofa and getting down on his knees to look under furniture.

Christina pitched in and searched, too, but she couldn't help grumbling that he could have bought some medicine at the convenience store.

"Couldn't," he said, eavesdropping on her mutterings. "Money's in my wallet, too.

"Got it." Greg stood up from behind the chair he'd sat in at dinner last night. Then, without even bothering to get a glass of water, he popped two capsules into his mouth and swallowed.

"Did you just take that on an empty stomach?"

Greg stuffed the wallet into his hip pocket. "Sure, why not?"

She looped her arm through his and guided him to the kitchen. "Come on, I'll fix you some eggs so that stuff doesn't eat a hole in your stomach."

Four eggs, two slices of toast made from last night's homemade bread and several bacon strips later, Greg pushed his plate away. The headache was gone, though he wasn't sure whether it was due to the pain medicine or the breakfast, but now another portion of his anatomy hurt.

It happened every time he looked at Christina. She was so beautiful, all sexy and rumpled looking in that shirt that proclaimed, "Protect The Ozone—Plant A Tree." Her hair was wilder than usual, not exactly curly but going in all directions, nevertheless. And her eyes still held a hint of sleepiness. He wondered if slumber had eluded her last night, just as it had him.

"Thanks for the breakfast." He got up and rinsed his dishes, stacking them neatly by the sink. "You'll make a good mother someday."

She eyed him with caution, as if she wasn't sure how to take his compliment. He didn't blame her. He hadn't given her much reason to trust him, having pushed her as hard as he did at dinner last night.

But he couldn't just let the moment slide by without trying to show her what a mistake she was making by divorcing him to marry Donald. If he didn't at least try to convince her that *he* was her Mr. Right, then he'd never be able to forgive himself for letting her enter a loveless relationship.

What could she have been thinking when she said yes to such an arrangement? He wanted like hell to ask her where her brain had been when she'd made that decision. Wanted to press her for an answer until she gave it to him fully and honestly...and then changed her mind.

But he wouldn't get anywhere using that kind of tactic. It hadn't worked last night, and he doubted such a move would fare any better this morning. But that wouldn't keep him from trying other tactics at other times. He had a lot to accomplish with Christina Cline and a short amount of time in which to do it.

"I'd better go now and let you get ready for work."

She walked with him to the foyer. "Is your headache better?"

"Somewhat." He held the door for her and stepped out onto the front porch. It wouldn't be completely gone until they were saying goodbye in the mornings like any other married couple going about their day. He wanted to kiss her and tell her he'd be home in time for dinner. That he would take the baby for his pediatrician appointment next week and change the oil in her car over the weekend.

Inside, the clock radio switched on and poured music out of Christina's open bedroom window. The happy, old-fashioned song captured his sentiments exactly, reminding him of the first time he'd met Christina. Yes, even then, when he saw her, he knew they'd go together, as the song said, like a wink and a smile.

Without a thought to what he was doing, he took her hand and pulled her to him. Swinging easily to the music, he overcame her initial resistance, and in a moment they were both laughing and moving together and apart.

It thrilled him to see her laughing like this, like the Christina he used to know. When they were together.

The last strains of the music had barely faded away and the words of the next song bled into it. That was when he felt the vibrations on the porch steps behind him.

"You two look like you're having a lot of fun this early in the morning."

Greg turned around to find Donald eyeing

Christina, who was breathless and rumpled in her sleepwear. Unshaven himself, Greg supposed it must look like he'd spent the night here.

"Um, just being goofy," she said, fending off his unspoken question. But she was quick to reassure him that nothing untoward had happened between them. "Greg left his wallet here after dinner last night, and he stopped by this morning to pick it up."

Donald then turned to Greg and gave him a similarly curious look. Greg wouldn't blame him if he took a swing at him. Hell, he probably would if he'd been in Donald's shoes.

Although he'd wanted to convince Christina not to go through with the wedding, he didn't intend to hurt his new friend.

Donald stuck out his hand in greeting. "'Morning, Greg." Then, to Christina he said, "I just came by to offer you a ride to the gym. Since I'm going to be there all day anyway, I figured we may as well ride together."

"Sure, that'd be fine." She turned to go inside, then paused in the doorway. "Greg, I'll bring some of my herbal remedies in case your headache returns."

His headache had already returned and was walking into the house with Christina.

What was Greg up to now?

He could have just given her some money and sent her on her way but, no, he had insisted on coming along, too. Was he really that interested in buying toys for the baby-sitting room?

Then again, maybe he was wondering about her motivation for coming to the toy store. After all, it wasn't in her job description to supply the room with toys, but he *had* given her carte blanche to buy anything she thought was needed for the gym. And since she was waiting on a plant order, she had decided to spend her downtime helping with the final touches in preparation for the grand opening.

She picked up a stuffed teddy bear, gave it a little hug and placed it in the shopping cart next to a small assortment of children's books.

"No, you've got it all wrong," Greg said, placing the bear back on the shelf. "Kids don't want to sit around holding a toy...they want to *play*."

Christina returned the bear to the cart. "Some kids will miss their mom or dad and will need something cuddly to comfort them." Picking up a soft, floppy bunny, she threw that in as well. "But you make a good point about their wanting to play. Let's go to the next aisle and look at board games."

"You must mean *b-o-r-e-d* games," he said, grabbing her elbow and steering her in the opposite direction. "I see something I wouldn't mind having for myself."

That something was a Jumparoo, a large rubber ball with a grip handle on top. Greg took off his jacket and draped it on a nearby bicycle handle before straddling the ball and bouncing into the aisle. His necktie flapping with each hop and his hair falling across his forehead, he seemed unconcerned about how out of place he may have looked.

"I haven't played with one of these since I was a kid." His expression one of pure joy, he held his arms wide. "Look, ma, no hands!"

"Look out for that—" Christina cringed as he came within inches of toppling a stand-alone basketball net "—net."

He looked in the direction she indicated. "Hey, cool. Let's get one of those, too."

Christina stepped aside as he bounced toward her. She hoped he didn't knock anything over or, worse, crash into a customer. An older woman, possibly a grandmother shopping for her grandchild, walked past, her pursed lips a clear indicator of her disapproval.

"Greg, maybe you should get off now."

"Oh, sorry," he said, dismounting and handing the ball to her. "Your turn."

She stepped back, her hands upraised. "No, I don't think that's—"

"Oh, I know," he said, giving her a clever grin. "You want to try the Power Pogo."

And before she could protest, he had her standing on the pedals of the spring-action toy. Certain he would persist until she at least tried the thing, she gave a couple of feeble hops.

"Oh, you can do better than that. Here, let me show you." At that, he got another display model and put it to the test. "See if you can beat that!"

A couple of minutes later, Christina had forgotten

all about the other customers in the store and was fully focused on trying to best Greg's record by jumping higher than the second lowest shelf. She couldn't remember when was the last time she'd laughed this hard or enjoyed someone's company so much.

Breathless with exhilaration, she found that the fun ended much too soon when his interest was diverted to something on the next row and he put his pogo stick back where he'd found it.

"Hey, we could use one of those," he said.

Christina grabbed his forgotten jacket, tossed it into the cart and followed him to a playhouse filled with colorful plastic balls.

"Take your shoes off," he said.

"But I'm not dressed for—"

"Oh, come on, it's not like you're wearing a skirt."

By now he had already kicked his shoes off and fallen backward into the ball pit. He lay there making flying motions with his arms

What his mother must have gone through when he was a child!

"Oh, all right." Although she made it sound as though she was making a huge concession on his behalf, the truth was that she really wanted to carry on with the fun he had started.

And the cycle continued. With his ability to show her a good time and make her want more, it was no wonder she'd so readily accepted his spur-of-the-moment proposal ten years ago.

But she wouldn't think about that now. Instead, she

focused above her on the happy-faced clown adorning the ceiling of the play pit. Right now, she could readily identify with the cheerful character. Sinking down into the layers of balls, she relaxed her body and closed her eyes.

"Now, isn't this a lot more fun than squeezing a stuffed animal?"

Turning her head, she looked over at him, her heart feeling mellow and full. "Mmm, depends on the animal."

A dark-haired, olive-skinned toddler pressed his face against the mesh enclosure and gave a gurgling laugh. His mother quickly dragged him away from the fun despite his howled protests.

She wondered if Greg had looked like that as a youngster, and then her thoughts turned to what his children might look like. If she'd had children with him, would some of them be blond and fair-skinned like her? Or would his genes, just like his personality, take control so that his own stamp was indelibly imprinted on all of them?

With Donald, their children would probably look like a generic blend of the two of them, since her coloring and his were so similar.

Greg fanned his arms again, his hand brushing against hers beneath the plastic spheres. She didn't pull back, not even when he closed his fingers around hers and gave a gentle squeeze.

"Before we leave," he said, "let's order one of these. And some tumbling mats, too."

"Don't forget the play tunnel and punching bag."

"Wouldn't dream of it."

The tone in his voice when he said it made her wonder what he did dream about. Were his dreams, like Christina's, the kind that woke him at night with perspiration covering his body and a desire for something he couldn't—or wouldn't—name?

"You've ruined me for all my future assignments," she told him. "Anything after this will be dull by comparison."

"Then you'll have to come back and visit often. Oh, you'll have to come back anyway." He rose to his elbows and hovered over her. "Mrs. Odell's garden club is going to meet at the gym. She passed along an invitation for you to join, and I told her you'd be at the next meeting."

Now Christina sat up. "You can't do that. Our deal was over when she signed the lease."

"That's not why I accepted for you." He rose to a full sitting position and rubbed his chin. "After you told me about wanting to start your own business, this seemed like a good way to make contacts with people who might need your services. And she did say they need someone with your expertise to oversee the park beautification project. They can't pay much, but it would be a start."

He seemed so pleased with himself that Christina couldn't work up any anger over having been manipulated into further contact with the woman who thought they were a happily married couple. She appreciated Greg's thoughtfulness, but this meant she'd have to continue the farce a little longer…at least until the annulment. It certainly would look odd to the older woman, she thought, for Christina to be marrying Donald so soon after her divorce. But she wouldn't think about that now.

''You're always pushing, aren't you?''

He shrugged. ''Hey, when I see an opportunity, I go for it.'' He picked up a yellow ball and bounced it lightly off her head. ''For instance, these toys we're buying today…they're an investment in a future generation of exercising adults. Kids are so sedentary nowadays. I want them to know that exercise can be fun. And maybe in a few years they'll insist on having their own membership at the Body Shoppe.''

It seemed as though he was always planning and scheming…always looking for the big chance and working it to his advantage.

Like the marriage proposal to get what he wanted on the wedding night. And roping her into playing his adoring wife so he could persuade Mrs. Odell to sign the lease. And hiring her to do his landscaping, and now committing her to join the garden club…both presumably to continue the pretense that they were married.

What might he want next, and how might he force her to bend to his will so he could get it?

This time a green ball bounced off her shoulder, jerking Christina from her thoughts. ''Wake up, sleeping beauty. We have a whole store full of toys to finish testing.''

Another ball grazed her elbow. Her reverie broken,

Christina grabbed a ball and lobbed it at his chest. "You test them. I have work to do."

She started to rise, but he stopped her with a fast and furious pelting. As much in self-defense as a desire not to be outdone, Christina fired back, and their play soon dissolved into dumping the balls over each other's head.

Weak with laughter, she fell against him, and they collapsed together on the floor of the pit, half buried in the plastic toys.

Lying against him, her eyes still damp and her ribs sore from the exertion of laughing, she was aware of the hard ridges in his abdomen where her arm was flung. And his calf muscle seemed like a rock where it pressed against her thigh.

"Is there anything I can help you folks with today?"

Peering into the play pit was an older man in the store's trademark red-and-white striped shirt and a name badge that read, John Highland, Manager.

Unperturbed, Greg didn't move a muscle from their undignified position. "Yes, I'll have one of these and a swing set," he said as seriously as if he were conducting a high-powered business transaction, "and my lady friend here would like a Mr. Boffo punching bag."

The dinner with Donald's parents had been a successful disaster. The meat loaf went over well with the Winklers, and they seemed to enjoy discussing the final preparations for the wedding.

Donald, on the other hand, had been a bundle of nerves, fussing over the food, fidgeting with the music selection on the CD player and giving Christina strange looks that she couldn't decipher. It was the first time since she'd known him that she had seen him find fault with anything. That night it had seemed as though nothing suited him.

And, to make matters worse, he kept trying to monopolize the conversation with talk of the new sideline career he'd found for Trina as a department store live mannequin. Acting as her agent, Donald was also looking into some local television and print advertisement modeling opportunities for her.

Though his parents had tried repeatedly to steer their dinner conversation back to the wedding, he had steadfastly kept returning to his new endeavors as a talent agent.

And now his nervous energy was put toward pacing the sun porch. She patted the cushioned seat of the wrought-iron chair beside her. "Why don't you sit down and enjoy your coffee while you tell me about your day?"

Donald reluctantly sat down and sipped the coffee but was soon up again, pacing the floor.

"If something is bothering you, maybe you should tell me about it." Christina pinched a dead leaf off the banana plant and set it on the table to toss out later. "I don't know enough about legal matters to offer any advice, but maybe by trying to explain the situation you'll come up with a solution."

Donald paused in front of her and shoved both

hands into his pockets. The coins in his right pocket jingled with his agitation. "It's not work."

"Then what is it?"

She stood up, and he abruptly sat down. When she rejoined him at the table, he rocketed out of the chair and started fidgeting with the sun shade. The cord had wrapped itself around the bamboo roll, suspending it on one side at the top, so he busied himself with unhooking the tangle.

A certain unease gripped the pit of Christina's stomach. "Your father's angina. Is he all right?"

"Dad's fine." He had his back to her as he jiggled the cord again. "It's me."

"You're sick? Donald, what's wrong?" Christina was on her feet, wanting to comfort him, but he kept his back turned to her, and she knew the news must be terrible if he couldn't bring himself to face her.

"Nobody's sick," he said quietly. "It's about the wedding."

And then she knew. The funny feeling she'd been having lately, the furtive glances when he was at the gym and his dropping his usual weeknight visits because he was "too tired." They all added up.

"It's Trina, isn't it?"

He stiffened, seemingly paralyzed by his indecision over how to answer. Then, recovering, he slowly reached for the rolled shade. "I'm not sure what you—"

"You're in love with Trina, aren't you?"

CHAPTER SEVEN

IN THE next instant, his hand slipped and landed against the screen. The shade fell off its anchor, splitting the screen above the patch.

And with it, her plans for marriage and children toppled. Donald didn't have to speak the words—he'd given his answer.

She was disappointed, no doubt about that, but despite the hollow feeling inside that threatened to swallow her, Christina felt no animosity toward either Donald or Trina. Since he'd started working at the gym, he'd practically glowed with happiness, a condition she had naively attributed to his working in his chosen area of accounting.

And she couldn't blame him for appreciating the adoring looks from a woman as attractive and sweet as Trina.

They were an odd match—perky, flamboyant Trina and quiet, staid Donald—but somehow they seemed to suit each other. There was something special between them…something that transcended parental approval, political aspirations, and even a desire for children.

She crossed to him and stilled his fumbling hands with a light touch. ''She's a wonderful girl,'' she said sincerely. "I want you both to be very happy together."

Donald turned toward her and cupped her hand in his. "Christina, I'm so sorry. I didn't mean for this to happen any more than you meant to rekindle things with Greg."

She jerked her hand away. "I don't know what you mean. There's nothing between—"

He shook his head, silently refuting what she'd been about to say. "There's nothing between *us*...you and me—" he stepped closer and laid an arm around her shoulder "—except a very close friendship that I hope will last forever."

When she looked up at him, his eyes were moist. As were her own. She wished him well. He was a good person, and he deserved more than she would have been able to offer him.

She sighed, the sound mixed with regret and relief. "Looks like we have a wedding to cancel."

He nodded and removed his arm from her shoulder. "I suppose so."

"Your mother's wedding dress. I'll return it—"

"There's no hurry." Donald avoided her gaze. "If you don't mind, I'd appreciate your not saying anything about this. Not yet anyway. My mother—" He looked down at his hands.

"Of course," she promised. "Just tell me when you're ready." She understood that he wanted time to break it gently to his family. And to prepare them to accept Trina as their future daughter-in-law.

The awkwardness seemed to hang in the air between them.

"Listen, if you need a godmother for your children," she said, breaking the uncomfortable quiet, "I'm told I'm good at nurturing."

With that, Donald laughed—something he seemed to be doing a lot of lately—and the tension was broken.

"Good luck, Donald." She hugged him, and he returned the gesture with more enthusiasm than he'd ever shown in the past. "I wish all the best for you and Trina."

"And I know you and Greg will be very happy."

She started to correct him but decided against it. There was no future for her and Greg. For one thing, he hadn't expressed an interest in salvaging their long-remiss marriage. And the few hints he'd made in that direction were said with an angle toward safeguarding his lease.

But explaining that to Donald would serve no useful purpose. She was certain he already felt plenty guilty about falling in love with Trina while engaged to her. If it helped him—even a little bit—to think their breakup had been mutual, then she saw no need in correcting his mistake.

They lingered a moment in each other's arms as they said goodbye to the dreams they'd built together. Donald would go on, she was sure, to a life in Fair Oaks with Trina, two or three children and a promising political career.

And Christina would go on.

A black, sporty convertible pulled up in the driveway, and two horn honks encouraged them to break the embrace.

Greg got out and walked toward the house, a slip of paper in his hand. "I didn't mean to interrupt your lovey-dovey stuff," he said, "but I thought you'd like to see what else I ordered for the baby-sitting room."

Stepping onto the porch, he showed them a page ripped from a catalog. There, in full color, were a miniature treadmill, exercise bike and rowing machine.

"The little rascals will love these because they'll get to exercise just like mommy and daddy," he enthused. Then he added with smug satisfaction, "And I'll have helped hook a future generation on fitness and exercise."

And bend them to his will to join the Body Shoppe, Christina mentally finished for him.

And the beat went on.

Christina's hiccups stopped the very next day. The months-long daily occurrence disappeared as suddenly as it had started. Even a heated encounter with Greg over whether to install white or floral-patterned curtains in the showers failed to bring on a new attack. It seemed as though her body knew, better than her mind or her heart, what was right—or, in this case, wrong—for her.

She made a half turn in front of her bedroom mirror and took a mental photograph of the image. Mrs Winkler's white dress billowed around her on the floor, and Christina imagined herself as she would have looked on her wedding day. This would have been a white wedding in every sense of the term, the spotless dress a symbol of the virginity she had saved all these years, and a minister sanctioning the union in Donald's church. She would have to return the borrowed dress, but for now she indulged herself in one last fantasy of a real wedding with all the sentimental trimmings...including a gold wedding band, a cake and rice thrown as she and her new husband embarked on their honeymoon journey together.

She smoothed a hand over a lump of fabric at her side. The seams bulged slightly where the dress had been taken in to accommodate her small frame. Like her relationship with Donald, it hadn't been a perfect fit, but she had tried to make adjustments. She made a mental note to remove the alteration stitching before returning the dress to Donald.

Reaching for the concealed zipper in the back, she managed to get it halfway down before it stuck. Twisting and writhing to gain better access, she only managed to get the zipper teeth more firmly embedded in the loose threads that had trapped it in the first place.

Frustrated, she stopped and took a deep breath. Having tried the dress on for one last memory to hold on to, she grimaced to think that this little fiasco would be part of that memory as well.

Before she could decide how to get out of this predicament, the doorbell rang. Good! Maybe it would be Donald.

She started for the hall and then paused. No, it wouldn't be him. And even if it was, wouldn't he think it odd to find her in his mother's wedding dress *after* they'd broken up?

The bell chimed again. Maybe it was Trina.

No, that wouldn't do, either. Asking for her friend's help could make for a very awkward situation. And if it was her parents, letting them see her in the wedding dress would build up their anticipation, only to have their happiness dashed to bits by news of the broken engagement.

This time the bell rang several times in succession. She considered ignoring it in the hopes the visitor would come back at a more convenient time, but it seemed obvious this person knew she was home and wouldn't let up until she came to the door.

Peeking out the small pane in the door, she saw none other than Greg grinning back at her.

"I'm indisposed," she called through the closed door. "Come back later."

He wrinkled his brow. "You're in the stove?"

Christina bit her lip. She already felt foolish for having gotten stuck in this dress, and she didn't want to compound her humiliation by having him see her this way. Maybe, if she sent him away and worked with the zipper some more, she'd be able to get out of this mess by herself.

Hiding behind the door, she opened it a crack and peeked out. "This isn't a good time. Can you come back later?"

"I brought some wallpaper border samples to get

your opinion on,'' he persisted. ''It'll only take a few minutes.''

Not having bothered to put on a slip, Christina now felt the stiff inner lining scrape across her sensitive skin. Picking wallpaper wasn't in her job description, but a lot of the work she'd done for Greg had been outside the boundaries of her normal duties. ''Couldn't you have shown them to me at the gym?''

''Sure, but then we wouldn't have been able to look at them over dinner.'' He glanced at his watch. ''Can you be ready in a half hour?''

Christina sighed but maintained her firm hold on the door. Tired of always bending to the will of others, she particularly wasn't interested in becoming a pawn in another of Greg's little agendas. ''Show them to me tomorrow,'' she said, hoping he would bend to her will for a change. ''I need some time alone tonight.''

And maybe the rest of the week. Who knew? Maybe she'd even be alone for the rest of her life.

Greg turned a curious eye to the woman who was acting so strangely today. She seemed upset. And then there was the matter of her headgear. ''What's with the veil?''

Her mouth formed a surprised O as she reached up to touch the lace adornment.

And then he noticed the salty trail on her cheek. ''You've been crying,'' he stated and pushed his way in despite her resistance.

''No, I haven't.'' Even so, she rubbed her eyes as if to erase any lingering evidence.

She stood before him, looking more beautiful than he remembered ever seeing her, dressed in the gown she would wear to marry another man.

The sight hit him in the gut like a medicine ball he hadn't braced himself for. But his feelings were not the issue right now. Christina was unhappy, and he wanted to know why.

"What's going on?"

She scratched her abdomen. "I'm stuck. I was trying the dress on to see what it would have—" She stopped herself. "The zipper's jammed."

"Well, hell, why didn't you say so? I can help with that."

She hesitated a long moment before she turned around and presented her back to him. He wouldn't be surprised if she'd used that pause to consider the propriety of having him, rather than Donald help her.

He fumbled a moment with the nylon fastener, but it held fast. His fingers were shaking, and he realized it was not so much from trying to get the tiny pull tab to obey his large fingers as from thinking about their own long-ago wedding. She should be wearing this dress for him. Maybe, if he had played his cards better, she would be renewing her vows with him instead of marrying another man. And he would be the one helping her out of the dress on their wedding night.

Once again, he reminded himself he had played his cards the best he could. He was proud of what he'd accomplished in such a short time, however, he could have done better if he'd been dealt a better hand. But he'd never been one to fret about could-have-beens, and he wouldn't start now.

The zipper finally released its grip, revealing to Greg as he slid it down the length of her spine to the top of her buttocks the reason for Christina's earlier hesitation in accepting his help. She wasn't wearing a bra.

Clutching the dress to the front of her, she turned and almost ran toward her bedroom. "Thanks," she said over her shoulder. "I really appreciate your help."

He was supposed to stay here in the foyer while she finished making herself presentable, he knew, but he'd seldom done what he was supposed to do. He followed her to the bedroom and found her pulling the veil from her hair. Propped in the middle of the bed was Murdock. Hairpins clattered to the hardwood floor, and she flung the sheer lace confection onto the dressing table. Then she covered her face with her hands and slumped wearily where she stood.

"Christina?"

Her startled response told him he'd caught her with her guard down.

"Is there anything I can do?" he asked as gently as if he were coaxing a frightened kitten out of a tree. "If you want to talk, I'm a good listener."

She turned and faced him, the pain etched deeply into her beautiful face. She was hurting, that was clear, and he wanted to take away the ache that was evident in her eyes. He would gladly shoulder the burden himself, if only he knew how.

But he didn't know how. Instead he fell back on instinct and opened his arms to her. Mindless of the dress sagging around her shoulders, she leaned into him as he wrapped her in his embrace.

Resting his chin against her hair, he felt the tension in her body slowly ease away. Still holding her, he moved so that they now sat at the foot of the bed.

"I'm sorry for being so silly," she said, brushing a hand across her cheek. "I'm not usually this emotional."

"It's okay." He squeezed her against him and was pleased when she didn't pull away. "Lots of brides have prewedding jitters."

He dared not hope that she was also having cold feet. He didn't think he could stand the disappointment if it wasn't so.

"No, it's not that."

He waited, but she didn't elaborate, and he wouldn't press her. It felt so good to sit here with her and feel her small body curving against his.

Without thinking of what he was doing or what the consequences might be, he lowered his head and lightly touched his lips to her cheek.

She turned toward him, and her mouth met his, setting off a chain of events that trailed feathery kisses from lips to chin and down to the hollow of her neck.

Her arms went around him, and the dress slipped lower, inviting Greg to explore the small hollow that disappeared beneath the satiny fabric. His desire straining his patience to the barest of threads, he pushed aside the frustrating fabric.

Her head back and her eyes closed as she opened herself to his loving touches, Christina sank into the mattress. The garment out of his way now, Greg plundered the tiny valley that had so intrigued him. As he kissed each small breast, trailing his tongue around the tempting pink centers, he felt her fingers roam up his neck and curl into his hair.

Blazing a hot path to her bare, smooth belly, he felt her draw in a quick breath. Her heated response spurred him on, and he pushed the dress down farther still, until its own weight pulled it to the floor. Christina squirmed beneath his tender ministrations, and her hands moved to his shirt, where she released each button with agonizing slowness. Undoing his pants, he hastily discarded the unwanted clothing and eased the strain that had been building since he'd stepped through the door.

Christina arched against him as he bent over her, and Greg was afraid he'd lose all control as his body sought to join hers. He slid a finger beneath the elastic waist of her panties and nudged them over her round hips.

He wanted to touch her, see her, experience her fully as they finally culminated what had been started ten years ago. Allowing his gaze to roam the length of her, he took in the firm swells of her breasts, the dip of her waist, the pale brown triangle that beckoned him to savor its delights and the tantalizing bend of her knees where her legs dangled off the bed.

As he pushed the scrap of silk over her thighs, his attention was snared by the thin green ribbon that wove its way around the waistband and ended in a miniature bow at the center of the lingerie.

A bow. Like a gift-wrapped package. The image cooled him as surely as if someone had doused him with ice water. She had waited twenty-eight years to share this gift with her husband on her wedding night. Greg was still her husband, but only on a technicality. And this wasn't even her wedding night.

Worse, he wasn't Donald.

Going to bed with a man was a major commitment for Christina. She wanted him now, he knew, but in the morning after the dewy glow of lovemaking had worn off, she would regret not having stayed true to her choice for a wedding-night surrender of her virtue.

Greg wanted to know—needed to know—that when she made love to him, it was with her fullest commitment. And that it was forever.

When he thought of what he'd almost done, Greg raked a hand through his hair. Shifting his weight off of her, he sat up, trying to let logic and sanity take control of his muddled thinking. He would still win her, he vowed, but not like this.

Christina blinked, her confusion readily evident over his abrupt change of mood. "Greg, what is it?"

He stood and paced the floor a moment before gathering his wits enough to collect her slacks and blouse from the back of her dressing chair and tossing them to her. Then he retrieved his own clothes and pulled them on as quickly as he could manage—before he changed his mind and finished having his way with her, commitment be damned.

He should be proud of himself, doing the right thing for a change, but all he felt was shame for almost having taken advantage of Christina when she was hurting and vulnerable. And he'd succeeded in hurting her worse.

"There's no point in letting this go on," he said, tucking his shirt into his pants. "I apologize for not acting like a gentleman."

As much as he wanted to hold her, beg her forgiveness and kiss away the quivering pout that had formed on her lips, he forced himself to leave now…before he did any further damage to the one person he loved more than life itself.

The shock and pain in her eyes as she sat on the bed holding the blouse in front of her haunted him as he stalked out of the house.

For a moment, Christina sat in stunned paralysis as the magnitude of what had just happened seized her. And then, shoving her arms into the sleeves of her blouse and pulling on her slacks, she raced to the door, determined to stop Greg. Determined that he quiet the roiling passion he had caused to rage within her.

"Greg, wait!"

Her shirt was untucked, only one button holding it closed, but that didn't stop her from dashing outside to tell him…

The top was down on Greg's car as he pulled out of her driveway and gunned the engine. The wind caught the shaggy fringes of his hair, lifting it in a farewell salute as his car sprinted down the street.

...she didn't know what she would have told him. Perhaps if she'd broken her promise to Donald and told Greg about the broken engagement he would have stayed, but something in her gut told her that wasn't the case.

The car turned the corner and moved out of sight. Trudging barefoot across the grassy lawn, she went back inside and threw herself on the sofa. One hand behind her head and the other trailing the floor, she stared at the giant painted sunflower that failed in its weak effort to cheer her up.

"Greg was right," she said aloud. "That painting is the pits."

And so was her self-esteem. What was it with her and men? True, she had wanted to wait until her wedding night to sample what, to many others, was just a part of the dating ritual. But she could have been swept off her feet.

Would have been swept off her feet if only Greg hadn't suddenly pulled the rug out from under them.

He was a man who was expert at bending others to his will and taking what he wanted. He took what he wanted and considered the consequences later, if at all.

Christina sat upright on the sofa. Could he have changed that much?

It was obvious that he wanted her as much as she wanted him. So why would he stop?

Unplanned pregnancy was the first and most obvious reason that popped into her mind. She hadn't been prepared to prevent such an occurrence, but she'd always thought most men carried those foil packets in their wallets. Then again, condoms weren't one hundred percent effective, either.

Could he have been worried that a baby would tie her to him? Making love was for a night, but a baby was forever.

Or… Christina stood and walked to the kitchen for a glass of water. Maybe he *had* changed in a way that she hadn't considered before. Maybe he was doing the honorable thing.

Christina downed most of the water, then splashed the rest of the cold liquid on her face.

If that was the case, she thought, why did he have to start being honorable now?

CHAPTER EIGHT

THE gym was abuzz with activity. Outside, people came and left, and several women—one with a toddler—enjoyed the early June Saturday.

Inside, people swarmed over the exercise equipment, hovered around the juice bar for complimentary smoothies, or waited their turn for the tanning bed. It felt good to see the fruits of their labors—of Greg's dream—come to such success.

Stepping aside for a college-age fellow intent on towel-snapping his companion, Christina made her way to the aerobics room. She'd already seen Donald out in the lobby, but he'd been so busy signing people up for membership contracts that he only had time for a smile and a wave.

As she opened the door and stepped inside, hyperactive music blasted, encouraging the dozen or so exercisers to move faster and try harder. Among the group of sweating women, Trina bounced near the front of the class, her ample endowments doing calisthenics of their own.

Christina watched for a moment as they began cool-down exercises, then gave a little wave to her friend before heading back out.

Her job at the gym over, Christina had come to say her goodbyes and leave for good. At the garden club meeting this week, it had been announced that an anonymous benefactor had provided funds for beautifying the park. To her delight, Christina had been selected to take on the job. Following that, several club members had spoken to her about making over their private gardens. And all because of the work she'd done at the gym. She had a lot to thank Greg for.

As she headed back through the exercise room, she saw him leaning casually against a stationary bike, a television news camera focused on him and the "Around Town" feature reporter, Timonia Powell, holding a microphone near his face. He looked good in the navy exercise shorts that revealed thick calves and the light blue tank shirt that clung to his chest like bark on a tree.

Since that humiliating night a week ago when he'd walked out on her for the second time in her life, they'd maintained a strained politeness between them. She supposed she could have told him about her and Donald breaking up, but that would have accomplished little besides make it look like she was begging. She should have known better than to let the situation escalate to the point it did, and his comment had convinced her of that.

There's no point in letting this go on, he'd said, leading her to the conclusion there was no point in pursuing her unless he could get something out of their pairing.

But what could he want from her, especially now

that the lease was firmed up and his business opportunities looking good?

"A hometown boy makes good," the reporter said to the camera. "After having left town in disgrace eight years ago following a two-year jail term for robbery, Gregorio Primo has gone on to make money the honest way, with a chain of exercise and fitness centers."

Christina winced at the woman's callous words and saw that Greg's reaction was one of barely controlled anger. He'd fought so hard to live down the unfortunate blot on his past, and now this woman was putting it on display for the whole town to see.

Obviously pleased with herself for having turned up such juicy fare in her research, Timonia smiled her self-satisfaction at the camera, then turned back to Greg. "Tell us, Mr. Primo, did you find that the street smarts you picked up before and during your incarceration helped you in your later business dealings?"

A long pause followed as Timonia waited breathlessly for his answer. When he did speak, his words were slow and measured, and they seemed to be directed back at his interviewer. "In my life," he said, blatantly ignoring her reference to his jail time, "I've learned it's best to treat people the way you want to be treated. Eventually the good you do for others comes back to you."

With that, he looked pointedly at Christina. The reporter noticed where he had fixed his attention and cranked the screws even tighter. "Does that have anything to do with your hiring the daughter of the man who locked you away? Is that your way of getting back in Sheriff Cline's good graces?''

''We'll continue this interview after you think of some questions to ask me about the gym,'' he said and thundered over to Christina.

Grabbing her by the elbow, he escorted her outside. ''There's something I've been meaning to talk to you about.''

Pausing on the cement apron just beyond the front door, Christina glanced through the leaded side windows and saw that Trina, having finished her aerobics class, was talking earnestly to Donald. Turning her back to the door, she faced Greg.

''I'm really sorry about how that interview was going back there,'' she said. ''That reporter seemed to be out for blood.''

He ran a hand down the back of his neck and seemed to be trying to press the tightness away. ''She's just trying to do her job.''

Christina was amazed by his easy forgiveness. He disregarded the harm that may have been done by the overeager woman's thoughtlessness just as he'd accepted the fate her father and the justice system had dealt him. In all that time she'd never heard Greg speak a harsh word against her father. And that was even after the older man had made that horrible comment about her casting pearls before swine.

''Don't worry about Timonia Powell.'' The tension that had grown between Christina and Greg now seemed insignificant, and she wanted to reassure him.

"You've done well for yourself, and lots of people will respect that."

And him as well. Despite the reporter's comments about his past, Christina had no doubt he'd earned the respectability that was so important to him.

"What are you going to do," he asked, "now that your assignment at the Body Shoppe is over? Does Linda have a fun new job in store for you?"

Christina dropped her gaze to the ladybug that landed on his shoulder. "Your success has inspired me," she said, meeting his eyes again. "I've given notice at Plants Plus and will soon be self-employed." With a little laugh, she added, "And poor."

"Hang in there." He touched a finger to her chin. "You're a hard worker and smart, too. It's only a matter of time before people realize you're the best."

Remembering what he'd said about wanting only the best for himself, she wondered if she would ever find a man who considered her "the best" as a potential wife. She sighed. Maybe she should just give up her silly dream of marrying Mr. Right. For, why would a Mr. Right want to marry someone who wasn't Miss Right?

"If there's anything I can do—"

"You already have. The bonus you gave me is going to help me through the lean times until business picks up."

"Good luck. I'm sure you'll do fine. Meanwhile, I'll try to send some clients your way." With that, he bent and gave her a light kiss on the lips.

Christina closed her eyes, knowing this would be

the last time she'd see him at the place they'd worked on together.

"Stay in touch." He gave her another quick kiss and grinned at her. "There's no need to go another ten years before we see each other again."

She started to say, "But that was your choice," but she wisely held her tongue. Unlike Timonia Powell, she had no desire to fling his past in his face.

His gaze left her, and his attention was now sharply focused behind her. "What the—?"

Storming past her, he flung open the front door and hastened inside. A glance through the window told Christina all she needed to know.

Donald was kissing Trina the way a man kisses the woman he loves.

Hurrying after Greg, Christina went inside just in time to see him haul Donald off Trina.

"Don't you have any sense of decency?" he said, holding Donald by the collar. "Are you trying to humiliate Christina?"

Donald tried to explain, but his words fell on deaf ears. "Christina doesn't mind. Honest!"

Greg drew back his fist. Simultaneously Trina called out "No!" and Christina jumped on Greg's back. The unexpected weight combined with her tugging at his ears threw him off balance, and he missed his punch.

The noise level in the reception area rose as bystanders egged them on.

"Stop it," Trina called, but her voice was almost muted by the cacophony. And since he wouldn't stop, the secretary grabbed his wrist, Christina still clinging like ivy to his back, and was flung aside as he made another attempt at Donald.

"We have an understanding!" Donald's voice broke through the din, and through Greg's thick head as well. Greg staggered to a stop, Christina still wrapped around his waist like snap beans on a garden stake.

It was then, during the momentary stillness, that Christina noticed the cameraman standing on her ficus tree planter to get a better shot of the action.

So much for respectability, she thought wryly. And so much for her reputation as a professional.

The steam now evaporated from his initial anger, Greg stood stock-still and assessed what he'd just heard. Shrugging her off his back, he rubbed an itch below his jaw and dislodged a ladybug.

"You have an understanding?" he said in stunned disbelief. "What the hell does that mean?" With a sickening feeling in the pit of his stomach, he suspected he already knew. It was clear there was little or no passion in their relationship, so it seemed Donald had arranged to look outside for what he wanted. How could any man be foolish enough to play around on such a prize as Christina? Remembering her dried tears the night he'd found her in the wedding dress, he wished his punch had found its mark square on Donald's nose.

As if reading his thoughts, Christina smoothed a hand over her mussed hair and quietly said, "I know all about Trina. It's okay. We're working it out."

He supposed she might be trying to smooth over the situation and make it appear less ugly than it was. Or, most likely, she was trying to help Donald save face. She was like that...always thinking of others first. Even when they didn't deserve it.

It made him want even more to put her on the receiving end of such caring for a change. He wanted to comfort her and give her the fuss and attention she so richly deserved.

''You have an understanding,'' he said again, hating the position Donald had put her in. ''He's not good enough for you, Christina. You need to dump this loser.''

As far as he knew—since he hadn't yet signed any papers to the contrary—she was still married to him. And he would redouble his efforts to try again...to make amends for the foolish mistake that had taken him away from her.

Greg hoped there wouldn't be any problem as he set out in earnest to win Christina back.

With a little luck and a lot of persistence, maybe he could persuade Christina to try again with him...and give up on her plans for the annulment.

Christina would have left immediately after that fracas in the reception area, if only she hadn't left her organizer book in Trina's office.

It was probably a good thing that it happened. After seeing Greg's interview and feeling his pain about reopening the past, she had found herself softening to him. The problem was, the more she softened, the more easily he could bend her to his will.

She didn't know what had been on his agenda when he asked her to accompany him outside, but right now she didn't even want to think about it. She just wanted to get out of here and put the Body Shoppe and Greg Primo out of her life and out of her mind forever.

Plucking the organizer off the shelf above Trina's desk, she opened it to the address section. There were a couple of potential prospects she wanted to contact in hopes of lining up their business. Since she had the rest of the afternoon free, she might as well stop by there on the way home and set up appointments with the managers.

Although she thought it sweet that Greg had stood up for her honor, she wished he hadn't caused a scene...a scene that would most certainly be played over and over until the TV station tired of it and moved on to the next scandal.

"Oh, good, you're still here." Greg stopped his headlong rush into the office. "I wanted to apologize to you for my behavior." Moving closer—too close for Christina's peace of mind—he paused a moment before continuing. "You were right. What goes on between you and Donald, or you and Donald and Trina, for that matter, is none of my business."

Christina flipped the page, pretending to be unaffected by him, but it was a difficult task. Why was it that his mere presence still made her heart flip, too? "Let's just forget about it, okay? Put it behind us."

"Just like everything else that's passed between us?"

Despite her wish to the contrary, Christina knew that things could never work out between them. Take now, for instance. Even after all the difficulties they'd been through, both in the distant and recent past, he still persisted in trying to make her give their relationship another chance. For all he knew, she was still engaged to be married, but that didn't stop him from trying to bend her to his will.

Couldn't he see that there were too many obstacles for them to overcome? Couldn't he see that they were just too different to ever be compatible with each other? That scene in the lobby was a perfect example of how he caused her to behave in ways that were unlike her. She still couldn't believe she had jumped on his back and tugged his ears like a wild woman. She taught Sunday School, for crying out loud! What would her students think of her behavior if they saw that clip on the evening news?

"That would be best," she agreed. She tried to step around him, but he easily blocked her path, once again forcing her to bend to his will. "I have to go now."

True to form, he persisted. "Not yet. The reason I wanted to speak to you before all that...you know...stuff happened was to suggest that you meet my neighbor Jim Vogel."

His brown eyes probed hers, and she suddenly felt stripped as naked as when he'd helped her out of the wedding dress.

"Jim's a contractor for the new Truxilla Mall. When I mentioned you might be available to design something for him, he said he'd like to meet you."

She hesitated. Another nice gesture on Greg's part. Would it also have strings attached? The persistence she often found so frustrating in him had paid off for her with the park project, but she was also saddled with a working relationship with him that she didn't want. "I don't know..."

"Just talk to him."

The Truxilla Mall was a huge undertaking. A project that large would put her on her feet financially and give her welcome exposure that could lead to other assignments.

"You'd introduce us?"

"Sure, why don't you come now? I'm going there anyway." Then, as an afterthought, he added with a grin, "But no more piggyback rides."

It was probably a mistake to be spending more time in his company, especially after that incident this afternoon. It seemed as though every time she was near him, she came away with her heart bleeding a little bit more than the last time.

But it was a short ride to his apartment complex. And once they got there, his neighbor would be a stabilizing third party. What harm could it do? And if she was lucky, maybe the contractor would put in a good word for her with his other businesses as well.

When they got there, Christina was amazed by the understated elegance of the place. Rose and teal floral wallpaper in the lobby brought together the blue-green speckled carpet and the pink upholstered chairs by the elevator. The formal chandeliers and brass fixtures, although beautiful, didn't seem to fit Greg's casual style, and she supposed his living here may have been another attempt at respectability and acceptance.

Upstairs, they had been welcomed warmly into the Vogel apartment and offered drinks on the balcony overlooking the terrace.

Although their conversation had taken a mere twenty minutes, she would feel its effects for the rest of her career.

Out in the hallway afterward, Greg clapped her hand in a high-five. "I'm quite impressed with your work," he said, proudly parroting what the older man had told her. "You come highly recommended."

Christina smiled over at Greg. Despite his frustrating tendency to exert control over her, she found his enthusiasm encouraging. The whole time she'd worked with him at the gym, he was constantly coming up with suggestions for her to put to use when she launched her business. Although he was rather forceful in the way he presented them, he did have some good ideas.

"Thank you," she said, looking at the man who alternated between elating her and frustrating her. "I've no doubt who recommended me to Mr. Vogel. You've been very complimentary about the fitness garden and other things I designed for you."

Greg dug his keys out of his pocket. "My recommendation was only one of many," he said. "Vogel had already heard that you were the driving force at Plants Plus.''

Too pleased to respond immediately, Christina stood transfixed in the empty hallway. She had always tried to do her best, no matter how large or small the project might be, and her clients always seemed to be satisfied with her work. But never in her wildest imaginings had she considered that her reputation would spread so far. Opening her mouth to speak, she found herself at a loss for words, which seemed to be a common occurrence whenever Greg was around.

''You're tongue-tied,'' Greg said, breaking her stunned silence. ''You're very modest about everything you do.''

His comment had her thoughts spinning back to the two times she hadn't been so modest with Greg. It was too bad they were such opposites, she thought, because he sure had a way of igniting her emotions.

And her temper, she reminded herself, trying to put things back in perspective. With this wonderful business opportunity all lined up, it wouldn't do to allow herself to get distracted by Greg...or his smile, or the way he looked from behind when he didn't know she was watching, or the scar on his cheek that was now so faded she could only see it when he was close enough to kiss her.

''I've seen businesses come and I've seen them go,'' Greg told her. ''But knowing what you're capable of, I expect you'll give your former employers a run for their money.'' He chuckled to himself, as if he were a bloodthirsty spectator at a boxing match in which the underdog competitor was about to dethrone the reigning champion. "You're on your way," he said, beaming his pleasure.

"And I owe it all to you." She tilted her face up to meet his warm brown gaze. "Despite some of our, um, unpleasantries, you've been very good to me."

Reaching for his keys, he unlocked the door to his apartment. "Not as good as I'd like to be."

CHAPTER NINE

CHRISTINA stiffened. Was this the part where he showed her the strings attached?

"You have to admit, Christina, we make a good team...in lots of ways." He held the door open for her.

She stood without moving, wondering at the implication of his words. Was he suggesting that she owed him something? He should know her better than to think she would barter herself in any way.

"I should go home now." She should have driven her car instead of letting him talk her into riding with him. Without her own transportation, she was at his mercy.

"I'll only be a minute," he promised. "Just come inside and wait while I make a phone call, and then I'll take you home."

She paused outside his door, wondering if he was telling the truth or just seeking to bend her to his will once again.

Caution was the operative word in dealing with Greg. He'd already shown her how easily he could make her throw reason to the wind, make her willing to take down her limits and sacrifice for him whatever he desired.

"I promise. Just a minute...five, tops."

Once again betraying her better judgment, she followed him into his apartment. Inside, it looked as though he had hired someone to decorate the place. That someone, apparently aware of his Italian heritage, had smothered the apartment in the Mediterranean look. Marble columns set off the formal dining area, and grape clusters and vines adorned the borders of the walls. The dark, heavy furniture loomed imposingly from their positions against the walls. Once again, it was attractive, but it didn't seem like Greg.

The only thing that appeared to have been put there by him was the overstuffed recliner. Big and comfy, it seemed approachable, like its owner. And, like Greg, it showed signs of rough handling in its past.

''Make yourself at home. I'll only be a minute,'' he said and went into the kitchen.

Although she couldn't make out his words, she could hear his voice. Warm and vibrant, its rich sound stirred her in ways she wished she could ignore. After making a restless trip around the room, examining the vases on the tables and pieces of still-life art that covered the walls, she sank into his easy chair and waited for him to finish his phone call.

Her life had changed tremendously since Greg had come back into it. Most of those changes were caused by him. Unfortunately, she wasn't sure whether to thank him or blame him.

An ornate clock on the table beside her loudly ticked the seconds away, reminding her that she needed to get started on drawing up some ideas for the mall's food court. The park project would need more input from the club members, so she could wait on that.

As she turned to check the time, her gaze fell on a small silver frame inlaid with pale gray-blue mother-of-pearl. Like the recliner, the piece seemed out of place. Inside the frame, a faded instant snapshot showed a young couple embracing in front of a rose-trellis backdrop.

The photo, perfectly angled so it faced the person seated in this chair, was smudged around the edges, as if it had been carried in a wallet for many years and handled often before being placed in the protective frame.

So carefree and happy, the couple smiled at the camera, he in his black jeans and leather jacket and she in her white sundress. A button-eyed rag doll dangled from her arms.

The good old days, some people said when referring to the past. The days when a person could dream of happily-ever-after and expect it to come true.

Greg hung up the phone and rubbed the tension from his eyes. Time was slipping away. If he wanted to win Christina back—and spare her the fate of being paired with someone who would openly cheat on her and expect her to go along with it—then he'd have to act fast and push hard. For all he knew, this would be his last legitimate opportunity to see her before the wedding.

Drawing a deep breath, he returned to the sitting

room to find her in his favorite chair. "I have to be honest with you," he blurted. "That phone call was just an excuse to get you in here."

Her lips formed a perfect rosebud as she took in this information.

"What I mean is, I wanted to talk to you. You know, just because you made a choice in the past doesn't mean you can't change your mind now."

Dragging the ottoman closer to her chair, he sat on it and leaned toward her.

"I'm here for you, Christina. You and I, we're right for each other." When she gave him a skeptical tilt of her head, he brought out the hardball. "You've gotta admit, there's a lot of chemistry between us. That's something you'll never have with Donald.

"Come on, hon," he said, grabbing her hand and holding on even when she tried to retreat from his touch. "Let's give it one more try."

"Wouldn't it have been simpler," she asked dryly, "to offer to show me your etchings?"

"This isn't about sex. It's about you and me." Why did she have to go and misunderstand him? Now he would have to work harder to convince her that he wanted her because of who she was and not for what she had to offer him. "I know what you want, and I want to give it all to you, and more. Why do you think I got you involved in the garden club or introduced you to Jim? Because it's what you want."

He got up and walked to the corner hutch. Dragging a finger over the framed cameo sitting atop it, he struggled for the words that would convince her she belonged with him.

"Why are you doing this?" Christina asked, her voice small and uncertain. "What do you want from me?"

"All the things I've done, even the things that hurt," he said, thinking of their wedding day when he was foolish enough to let her go, "I've done for you. Because I care about you and because I want you to be happy."

"If you want to see me happy," Christina said, her tone in stark contrast to her words, "then all you have to do is look at this picture." Setting it back on the table in its place of honor, she folded her hands in her lap. "I was happy then. I was happy," she continued, her voice quavering slightly, "until you pushed me away."

"I was stupid," he said angrily. "If I had it to do all over again, I would do things differently."

It would have been difficult, letting her suffer because of his mistake and the black mark on his police record. And it would have been hard, working to overcome public opinion and find his way into the town's good graces, but they could have done it *together*. No matter how impossible it might have seemed for them to survive that two-year separation and the rebuilding of their relationship, it still would have been easier than watching her enter into a marriage with a man who could only hurt her worse than he himself had.

''You had that chance,'' she said softly. ''The night you and I almost made love.''

He could tell she was uncomfortable talking about it, but she pushed on anyway.

''When you left me, it was just like our wedding day all over again.'' She stood and picked up her purse. ''Which one didn't you want, me specifically or commitment in general?''

''It's not like that. You have to believe me.'' It tore at his gut to think that he had made her believe those terrible things. He crossed the room to her and drew her hands to his heart. ''I love you, Christina. That's why, when I remembered what you said about saving yourself for your wedding night, I couldn't take that dream away from you.''

Lifting a hand to his mouth, he kissed her smooth knuckles.

''I couldn't take that from you,'' he confessed, ''even if it meant that you would be giving your precious gift to a man who wouldn't value it as much as I do.''

He waited a long moment as his words sank in. She had to know what a sacrifice that had been for him.

''You belong with me.''

She looked down at her hands, where he ran his thumbs over her soft skin. ''I don't belong to any man, Greg. All my life, I've had people—including you—telling me what to do, and I complied because I wanted them to be happy. Well, I'm entitled to happiness, too.''

"Yes, you are," he agreed. Finally they were coming to some sort of understanding. That was what he'd been trying to tell her all along—that she needed to follow her heart in this serious matter of marriage. "You know you won't be happy with Donald. Call off the wedding, Christina, and forget about the annulment. If you'll be honest with yourself, you'll see I'm the right man for you."

He knew he was pushing her—and pushing hard—but dire situations required desperate measures. And, as he envisioned the possibility of Christina walking away from him forever, he felt more desperate than he had in his entire life.

When she lifted her face to him, her eyes gleamed with unshed tears. "The die is cast."

It felt as though his stomach had dropped into his shoes. "I'm losing you, aren't I? This time forever." If she turned him down now, no amount of work or impressing the townspeople with his new, squeaky-clean image would win her back. "Once you say 'I do' to Donald, it will be for life."

She nodded mutely.

And then his fear turned to anger. "You're giving your loyalty to a man who doesn't deserve it. A man who has already flaunted his mistress even before the vows are spoken and grown cold."

"It's not what you think."

"And he's not what you think he is. Can't you see what a mistake you're making? Donald can't give you what I can give you, Christina."

"This isn't about Donald."

She withdrew her hand from his and tried to move past him, but he held her by the shoulders, forcing her to heed his words…to consider her decision carefully. Before it was too late.

"Yes, it is about Donald," he insisted. "It's about what Donald can't give you."

She tried to squirm out of his grasp, but he held firm, trying to force her to see reason.

"When he kisses you, can he make you feel like this?"

He kissed her hard, trying with all he had to show her they were meant to be together. Her lips, like the rest of her, were soft but unyielding. But he could tell he had touched her inside…touched a part of her that was, at the moment, too stubborn to admit he was right.

"Two people who aren't in love can't conjure up the feelings we have for each other. What we have is too good to throw away." He was determined that she realize the truth in his words and the passion in his kiss.

She was resistant at first but, just as he'd hoped, she melted under the heat of his kiss. Pressing her to him, he laid a hand at her waist, compelling her to join him not only at the lips but along the length of their bodies. The dip and flare of her waist and hips made him want more than what they could give each other, standing in his living room. "I want you, Christina. And you want me, too."

There was so much feeling passing between them that he didn't see how she could deny it.

"Say yes," he murmured against her lips. Then, lifting his head he said, "Choose to be with me. Once you say yes, we can try again...pick up where we left off."

A shadow passed over her pale blue eyes. "Don't you see? That's what I've been trying to tell you all along. We *can't* pick up where we left off."

The die was cast, just as she'd said.

Seeing the torment etched on her face, he realized he'd been unfair to her. When she became engaged to Donald, she gave him her word. And Christina Cline did not go back on her word. But that didn't stop him from giving her one last try.

"You still love me. I can tell by the way you responded to my kiss."

She looked embarrassed and started to protest, but he surprised her by voicing the words for her.

"In your mind, I've abandoned you twice already, which means I could do it again. Considering what you've been through, I can't blame you for thinking I lack commitment." Unfortunately he had no way of proving to her that he wasn't that type of man. "At this point, you must think it's better to be cheated on by a man you don't love than abandoned by the one to whom you've given your heart."

She captured her lower lip between her teeth and looked down at the floor.

He wanted to tell her he wouldn't leave her again. He wanted to convince her that all the hard work that had gone into his gyms had been for her...they were proof of his commitment, even when he hadn't been with her.

But more than that, he wanted her to come to him of her own accord. Realizing his own selfishness in pushing her so hard, he stepped away from her and went to the coffee table.

"You were right about people always telling you what to do." Ever since he'd known her, he had encouraged her independence. From the beginning, he had pushed her to make up her own mind, even if it meant standing up to her father, the person she respected most. "I suppose, in trying to force your independence, I was just as guilty as those who took advantage of your easygoing nature."

Pulling open the coffee table drawer, he knew he had to let go completely and allow her to make her own choice. Even if that choice didn't include him.

Taking a painfully honest look at his own actions, he admitted, "My selfishness may have been what caused the problems between you and Donald, and I apologize for that." If he hadn't pursued Christina so aggressively, he wouldn't have raised doubts about her relationship with her fiancé. And if Greg hadn't kept her working so many overtime hours with him, he wouldn't have caused Donald to be tempted by Trina. "I don't want to stand in the way of your happiness."

Taking the papers from the drawer, he laid them on the table and signed them. As he handed the document to Christina, he was aware that he had surprised and possibly hurt her yet again.

"I'm setting you free," he said, "like I should have done before."

She opened her mouth to speak, but before she could say anything he told her, "I still love you. I'll always love you. And because of that, I'd do anything to make you happy. Even if it means giving you up."

He was, indeed, a changed man. He had done the right thing, and it hurt like hell, knowing she'd made her choice. But he was glad he did it.

She'd had her chance. What she'd been secretly hoping for the past ten years had finally been made available to her, and she'd passed it up. And now her insides seemed turned upside down.

Setting her cup of chamomile tea on the wrought-iron table next to the papers, she fought bravely against the tears, but they came anyway.

"Go ahead, honey, let it out." Trina passed her a clean tissue to replace the balled-up one she'd shredded to bits. "I'm here for you."

Christina blotted her eyes. "It took all my willpower to refuse him."

"Well, if your decision is making you this unhappy, maybe you should give him a call. Let him know you've changed your mind." She flashed Christina a brilliant red smile. "Besides, I think you two make the cutest couple."

Running a thumb over the cup handle, she thought about what her friend said. Sure, she and Greg had had fun in the beginning, but he had called the shots in their relationship, coercing her into doing things she never would have even thought of on her own. "It would never work out between us."

She sipped the hot tea, welcoming the burn as it scorched a path down her throat, proving that she wasn't numb inside as she'd suspected.

"But you enjoy so many of the same things."

Staring out into the dark, Christina told Trina what had been troubling her. "He has a way of talking me into doing things that are out of character for me."

Trina sat forward in her chair. "You don't mean he talked you into—"

"No, not that." But he easily *could* have. Christina felt her cheeks grow warm as she remembered practically begging him to make love to her. "For example, there was the time he insisted we make Murdock anatomically correct under the diaper. That was only one in a list of high-school pranks he involved me in."

The wedding, of course, was the biggie.

"And more recently, he roped me into working on his gym and acting like a kid at the toy store."

"Yeah, it's been fun, hasn't it?"

Christina gave up trying to explain the situation. It was so complicated, she wasn't even sure she fully understood it herself. The night air suddenly chilled, and the crickets chirped louder in anticipation of the summer storm that appeared to be headed her way. She stood to lower the roll-down shade, which, once again, got caught in the cord. "This just isn't my day."

The knot that had been forming in her throat almost

choked her, it grew so tight. Assuring herself she'd done the right thing, she barely managed to hold back the flood of tears.

"*Of course,* I did the right thing," she said more to herself than to Trina. "After all these years, I'll finally have the chance to be my own person—to make up my mind and follow my own lead instead of someone else's." Christina fumbled with the pull cord, to no avail. Dragging the chair over, she stepped on it to try to loosen the stubborn string. "After all these years, I will truly be free."

"Do you want some help with that?"

"No, I think I've got it." Her attention fixed on the troublesome shade, she vented her frustration over today's events. "This afternoon Greg was in peak form, manipulating my emotions to get me to bend to his will…just as he's always done. I dread to think how much worse his power struggles would have been if he'd known I was no longer engaged to Donald."

"That's sorta what I came here to talk to you about." Trina got up and walked over to stand beside Christina. "It's about Donald and me."

The tall blonde hesitated a moment, as if she feared Christina's reaction.

"Yes?"

Her words were barely more than a whisper. "He asked me to marry him."

Christina had expected this to happen, just not quite so soon. She leaned over and gave the statuesque woman a warm hug. "Oh, Trina, that's wonderful!"

"You're not upset?"

"Not in the least." And she meant it with utmost sincerity.

Trina pushed a yellow tendril behind her shoulder. "That's such a relief! You have no idea how I worried about telling you."

"You shouldn't have. I think you two will be good for each other." Although things hadn't worked out for Christina and Greg, she was glad that at least Donald had found a love that would see him through the years.

"There's one other thing."

Resting a hand on Trina's shoulder, she stepped down off the chair. Today had been full of unexpected happenings...what was one more surprise? "Fire away."

"Since no one ever canceled the church or the preacher, Donald and I thought we would make use of them. I realize the date is very close, but we want to get married as soon as possible." She followed Christina back to the table and sat down. "I just wanted to make sure you're okay with that."

"Go for it." She smiled, thinking what a pretty ceremony it would be in the historic old church. "What did Mrs. Winkler say about the sudden change in plans?"

Trina hunched her shoulders and looked embarrassed. "Donald hasn't told her yet."

Stunned, Christina slapped her hand on the table. "He hasn't told her about you?"

"Or about you. She still doesn't know you two broke up."

"I can't believe it. I know Donald wasn't looking forward to breaking the news to her, but I thought surely he would have mentioned it by now."

"It's not for a lack of trying on my part." Trina paused as if carefully considering her words before she spoke. "Once Mrs. Winkler makes up her mind about something, she can be very…um…persistent about having things her way."

Christina sighed. "I know the type."

"Anyway, when Donald's older brother planned to marry a girl from a different background, Mrs. W did her best to put a stop to the wedding."

She remembered hearing about the ordeal Donald's brother went through. Mrs. Winkler had made things so unpleasant that the couple had foregone their planned church wedding and eloped a month before the scheduled event. "She came around eventually. I understand she's very fond of her daughter-in-law now."

"Yes, but that was only after it was too late for her to do anything about their marriage. Which is why Donald wants to wait until just before the wedding to tell her." Trina touched a polished fingernail to her cheek, taking care not to disturb her makeup where she carefully scratched an itch. "But I wouldn't be surprised if he avoided it altogether. You know Donald. He hates confrontation."

And she knew Mrs. Winkler, who could be quite headstrong. She could see how he felt backed into a corner after all the difficulties she'd presented her older son.

"Enough about Donald and me. What about you and Greg?" Trina said, turning the conversation back to the subject Christina had hoped was dropped for good. "Hey, I know!" She held a finger up as she blurted out her idea. "We could have a double wedding."

"You haven't been listening." Christina got up again and gave a final tug at the shade's cord. "We're already married, and it isn't working."

Trina shrugged her disappointment. "*Hmph.* Seems like a good way to make a fresh start, if you ask me."

Of its own accord, the shade broke loose from its bracket, this time ripping the latest hole wider than the patch. The rusted metal fibers relented one by one, and the hole grew bigger until the top folded over and the entire section, patch and all, collapsed into the yard.

Christina stared for a moment before the dam of frustration finally burst. The emotions she'd managed to cork as she'd talked to Trina came rushing back to the surface in a force so overwhelming it took her by surprise.

"This is just like my life," she said, pulling the tissue from her pocket and blowing her nose. "Everything's falling to pieces and making a big mess."

Sitting on the porch floor, she gave in to the tears.

True friend that she was, Trina didn't make her feel silly for overreacting to a problem that was so minor on the surface. She seemed to understand that this went a lot deeper than a mere torn screen. She sat down in front of her, crossed her legs and stroked Christina's arm as she murmured, "There, there."

After a moment, Christina wiped her eyes. "I should have ripped out the old, damaged screen and replaced it with those new windows I wanted," she said. "With the heavy layers of rust on them, it's been difficult to see clearly through the screens." She sniffed lightly.

"You know, you're right," Trina said. "Polished, new glass would give this place a whole new perspective. Things outside would look brighter, and the jalousied windows would allow more sunshine inside."

"Oh my gosh." Christina placed a hand over her mouth. "You're talking about Greg and me!"

"No, hon, I was talking about the porch."

"Don't you see? Continuing my marriage to Greg could never work." She leaned back, surveying the damage. "Just like that rusted and ripped screen, our damaged relationship would never be strong enough to sustain our efforts to patch it up."

"You're tired. Maybe you should get some rest and think about this tomorrow. Things will look better in the light of day."

Thinking back to the problem that had been with them since the beginning, Christina knew it would be impossible to stay with someone who steamrolled her into doing things he wanted. "You're right. I'm going to be like Scarlett O'Hara and think about that tomorrow."

She got up and walked into the house, Trina right behind her. The watercolor sunflower over the fireplace seemed to glow a horrible mustard-yellow. Her father had talked her into hanging her mother's gift in the front room even though Christina would have preferred to put it somewhere less conspicuous.

Feeling defiant, she asked Trina to help her take it down and carry it to the spare bedroom.

"Good," the younger woman said. "I thought you'd never get rid of this hideous thing."

"Greg hated it, too. It was one thing we *had* agreed on, even though I hadn't wanted to admit it at the time." Covering the bare spot with the beautiful, antique mirror that had been replaced by the watercolor, she felt a sense of satisfaction and relief at having followed her own heart. "Even though Greg had pushed me to do this," she reluctantly admitted, "it was a push I needed—and for something *I* wanted."

Trina wiped her hands on her jeans and stood back to admire the new look. "Other than Donald, he's the most unselfish person I know."

It did seem as though he was always pushing her, but in hindsight Christina saw that all those pushes had been for things she had wanted—from their marriage to the garden club membership, and to quitting her job to strike out on her own. And even to his pushing her away when they'd come so close to making love.

"We've been on the same wavelength all along." Although she said the words aloud, she was talking to herself. Unfortunately she'd been resistant to his pushing because of their past. "And I've been too stubborn to admit it."

The problem, she finally saw, was the pushing that came from others about matters that were not dear to her heart. These, she had to learn to resist. Greg's pushes, she had to learn to accept.

"So what are you going to do about it?"

"Here's what I'm going to do." Going back to the spare bedroom, she retrieved one of the leftover invitations and brought it back to the living room. She flashed a conspiratorial smile at Trina, and with firm, decisive strokes of the pen, she addressed the envelope.

CHAPTER TEN

GREG stood in front of the church. The invitation in his hand indicated the wedding would take place at two o'clock Saturday. It was now three minutes after the hour, and the church doors were closed.

He'd wavered between coming and staying away. Maybe he should just take the closed doors as a sign for him to turn around and go back home.

Aw, hell, she'd invited him, so she must've wanted him to be there. And there was no way he could deny Christina anything she wanted, no matter how much it hurt him. Besides, he had to see the wedding for himself. Like a mourner at a funeral, he needed to put closure to this part of his life. And to say farewell to this person in his life.

Slipping quietly into the church, he took a seat on the back pew. He tugged the tie at his neck, but even that didn't relieve the suffocating feeling. Seeing the couple standing before the minister, he took comfort in knowing he'd done the right thing by setting Christina free. He'd always heard that if an experience didn't kill you it would make you stronger. If that were true, he'd be Mr. Universe by now.

From his vantage point, it looked as though Christina's dress fit better than it had the night he'd helped her out of it. Against his will, he pictured her as she had looked with the white frock slipping down off her shoulders. His body responded to the memory in a way that was inappropriate for someone in the hallowed halls of church.

Lifting his jacket sleeve, Greg grabbed a few arm hairs and yanked, hoping the pain would help take his mind off matters he had no business thinking about. And at Christina's wedding, no less.

In that white dress and long veil, she looked like the very essence of purity. And she was.

When the minister declared them husband and wife, Greg felt as though his heart had broken clean in half. And when the groom was invited to kiss the bride, he couldn't bring himself to watch. As Donald started to lift the veil, Greg looked away, focusing on the stained-glass window with the verse at the bottom that read, "…What things soever ye desire, when ye pray, believe that ye receive them, and ye shall have them."

He'd been doing that for years, but now he offered up one final, desperate prayer.

A scream split the air.

Greg's attention, along with everyone else's, was riveted to the front of the room, where Mrs. Winkler leaped to her feet and let out another blood-curdling cry.

Donald, frozen in the act of raising his bride's veil, seemed torn between kissing his new wife and attending to his panic-stricken mother.

Everyone else in the room may have been watching Mrs. Winkler's hysterics, but Greg's gaze was fixed on the bride with the shocking blond hair and two-inch eyelashes.

''Oh, Lordy, Lordy, Lordy!'' Mrs. Winkler wailed, and she swooned as though she was going to faint. His decision made, Donald dropped the veil and caught his mother in his arms.

Pulling the invitation from his pocket, Greg looked down at the handwriting on the envelope. The feminine loops and curls were definitely Christina's.

With a newfound surge of hope, he scanned the milling crowd and locked on Christina's beautiful face at the far corner of the room. It was clear she had been watching for him, and now she gave him a tentative smile.

Lifting his eyes heavenward, he murmured a heartfelt, ''Thank you!'' Rising to his feet, Greg pushed through the crowd and made his way down the aisle toward the front of the sanctuary.

Friends and family hovered around the woozy woman as Donald and his father both struggled to keep her from hitting the floor. With effort, they managed to seat her on the front pew, where the shocked woman shrieked, ''Donald, you didn't. Tell me you didn't!''

Leaning over the frantic female, Trina fanned her with the hem of her gown. ''I'll be a good wife, Mother Winkler. I promise!'' Then, to Donald, she added, ''You were supposed to tell her!''

Nearing the center of the hysteria, Greg found his path blocked by the curious onlookers and well-meaning helpers. He reached past someone and shook the startled groom's hand. "Good choice, Donald. Congratulations."

Then he pushed through to Christina who seemed swallowed up in the crowd. And when he reached her, he held her as if he would never let her go.

Christina returned the embrace, and he hugged her tighter.

"Greg," she said after a moment, her voice a tiny squeak, "I can't breathe."

With a laugh and a burst of willpower that he didn't know he possessed, Greg released her and led her to the side exit. They walked out of the church hand in hand.

A stand of oak trees shaded them from the warm June sunshine. Funny, Christina thought, how the birds seemed to be singing more cheerfully than usual today. Drawing in a deep breath, she told him the worry that had plagued her since she mailed the invitation. "I didn't think you'd come."

"Whenever and wherever you want me, Christina, I'll be there."

He looked so handsome in his navy suit. So masculine and so very desirable. When he looked at her like that, with his eyes hooded and dark, it made her want to kiss him, and be kissed by him for all of eternity.

But eternity was a long time away. And they needed to deal with the here and now before looking to the future.

"I have a lot to say," she confessed, "but I don't know where to begin."

Putting his arm around her shoulders, he started them walking along the perimeter of the neatly trimmed church lawn. Ahead, the honeymoon get-away car proclaimed, Just Married. "Why don't you begin by telling me why you didn't marry Donald?"

She sidestepped a honeybee enjoying a clover blossom. "At the time, I thought it was because I didn't want to stand in the way of Donald's chance for a happy-ever-after relationship. But deep down inside, I think it was because I was tired of going along with what other people wanted, even when it wasn't my heart's desire." She stared ahead, watching a squirrel chase another through the grass. "Donald and I drifted into our engagement because our parents pushed us to get married."

Greg waved away a flying insect that hovered too close, but remained silent, waiting for Christina to finish.

"You pushed me a lot, too," she said, "and it drove me crazy. But eventually I realized that you only pushed me to do the things I already wanted. In so many ways, I've found my heart's desire, and I owe much of that to you."

"That's all I ever wanted was for you to be happy," he said with sincerity. He stopped at a dogwood tree behind the church. With an eyebrow raised questioningly at Christina, he patted a low horizontal branch.

In answer, she stood before it, and he grasped her at the waist and lifted her onto it. A moment later, he climbed up beside her.

"I've told you why I didn't marry Donald. Now I need to ask you something."

He nodded, and she steeled herself against the pain and embarrassment that his answer might bring.

"Why did you marry me? Was it for the sex?"

He laughed so hard the branch shook beneath them. And then he put an arm around her waist and cuddled her close. "No, my sweet little Christina. As wonderful as sex with you might be, it would only have been the icing on the cake. If sex was all I wanted, I could have had that at any time."

That was true. He'd always had his pick of girls in high school. And later, when he came back to Morrison Heights, he could have had her, too. But he had ended their lovemaking because her wish for a memorable honeymoon encounter was more important to him than his own physical needs.

"But when we didn't finish our honeymoon, you wouldn't have anything else to do with me. I couldn't help but think—"

He touched her face, urging her to look at him. "I felt like I wasn't good enough for you. When your father took me away, I knew I had to clean up my act before we could try again."

"None of that mattered to me."

"I know, but it mattered to me. I didn't want people looking at us and thinking 'she could have done better.' I didn't want anyone looking down on you because of me."

"Oh, Greg," she said, leaning against his solid shoulder. "You've been so unfair to yourself."

He hugged her, and Christina imagined waking up every morning in his strong arms.

"So where do we go from here?" he asked. "Do you want to give our marriage another chance?"

She straightened and swung her feet, watching the folds of her dress flap with the motion. With a slow shake of her head, she told him, "I don't think that will work. We were too young when we got married, and we got off to a bad start."

"Are you saying our marriage isn't worth fixing?"

With a little smile, she said, "Sometimes you have to take the old rusty screen off your porch and put new glass windows in."

"What?"

"Let's stop trying to fix the past and just start fresh. Throw away the old and start all over, right from square one." Just as he'd been trying to do with his own past, they needed to put it all behind them and let today be the very beginning of their new relationship.

Taking her hand, Greg smiled at her, his face filled with the joy that Christina felt inside.

"This time let's do it right," she said.

He hopped down from the branch and stood before her. Giving a courtly bow, he extended a hand to help her down. "In that case, Miss Cline, may I have the pleasure of your company at a movie tonight?"

Christina lifted her chin and, with a coy turn of her head, said, "I'm sorry, sir, but I don't believe we've ever met."

The church doors swung open, and well-wishers

lined the sidewalk to Donald's soap-painted car at the back of the building.

Mrs. Winkler, throwing rice at the couple, seemed to have recovered from her shock. And when Trina impulsively stopped their departure to give her new mother-in-law a hug, Mrs. Winkler returned the gesture.

"Hark," Greg said, cupping his ear toward the activity. "I believe I hear some friends who would be happy to introduce us."

Giddy with happiness, Christina accepted his helping hand—this time willingly, because she knew they both wanted the same thing—and ran with him to the church.

EPILOGUE

TRINA bustled around Christina in the Morrison Heights Park gazebo, smoothing the floor-length skirt and checking to make sure all the seed-pearl buttons were fastened.

Then she tugged at the waistband of her matron-of-honor dress. ''The little rascal must be growing like crazy,'' she said, patting her belly. ''This dress had plenty of room a month ago.''

Christina smiled, happy for her friend's early success at starting a family. It had only been three months since Trina and Donald's wedding, and already the new bride was starting to show.

''Okay, let's run through the checklist.'' Trina picked up a clipboard and read off the first item. ''Something old?''

Christina touched the string of pearls at her neck. ''My great grandmother's necklace.'' The piece was an heirloom given to her by her father, along with an apology for the unkind things he'd said in the past.

''Something new?''

She fluffed her dress and curtsied.

''Something borrowed?''

At that, Christina lifted the dress to display the lace garter above her knee. ''Mrs. Odell insisted this would bring Greg and me many happy years to-gether.''

184

Trina made another check mark on her paper. "And what about something blue?"

"The asters in my bouquet."

"Here's a lucky penny for your shoe, and you're set, gal. Let's go get you married!"

As the music played and Christina began the march down the garden path on her father's arm, Greg gave her a heart-stopping smile. She couldn't imagine a wedding being more perfect—or more real—than this.

The groom was the best part about it, of course. He had insisted on having the wedding in this portion of the park, where they had been working hard all summer to make it as romantic as possible. And then he had seen to some of the wedding details, saying he wanted to make it "real" this time. And he'd done a wonderful job of it.

A white-painted trellis, adorned with fragrant peach-colored roses, had been positioned at the front of the natural sanctuary. This wedding, unlike their first, had been well publicized, and the white wooden benches were full, leaving standing room only. In a television interview about the garden club's efforts to beautify the park, Greg had issued an open invitation for everyone to come to the wedding, saying he wanted the whole town to know he was the luckiest man alive to be marrying Christina.

Sheriff Cline stopped in front of the preacher, then stepped back for Greg to take his place beside Christina. The two men paused a moment while her father shook Greg's hand warmly. It meant a lot to Christina to see her two favorite men making amends.

As the minister said the vows, Donald stood beside

Greg as the best man. And when it was time for Greg to place the ring on her finger, Christina felt her eyes moisten as her sentimental husband pushed the gold band over her knuckle. The crochet pattern in the gold resembled the pull-ring she'd worn at their first nuptials.

"You may kiss the bride."

Christina handed Trina her bouquet and turned to face the man who was now officially and without a doubt her husband. He lifted the veil from her face and brushed a tear of happiness off her cheek before kissing her...the way a man kisses the woman he loves.

His lips were warm and sweet, and his arms so strong yet gentle. When he broke the kiss, he chucked a finger under her chin. "Come on, let's get some cake."

It took her a moment to get her skirt straight to walk down the aisle with him. As she did, she saw, seated in the front row, a very special guest. Dressed in a miniature tuxedo, Murdock sat holding the original crocheted ring.

"The spice cake," Greg told her later as they cut the confection together, "represents us. It has enough zip to make things interesting."

Christina took a bite of the cake he offered her and licked the icing from her lips. "And enough sweetness that our relationship will always be like a special treat."

For an event that took so long coming, it sure was over in a hurry. The beribboned rice packets were soon distributed to all the guests. Mrs. Odell came up and offered them both a hug.

"It's so nice that you're renewing your vows." The older woman touched her locket, obviously remembering her own vows many decades earlier. "And it's so nice that you two could enjoy this special day amid the park improvements that your husband funded."

"Funded?"

Almost immediately, Mrs. Odell's eyes widened as she realized she'd let the cat out of the bag. "Oops!"

Christina turned to Greg while the guests waited for them to depart. "*You* were the anonymous benefactor?"

The expression he wore reminded her of the times he'd been caught playing pranks on teachers at school. Sheepish at having been caught, but not the least bit repentant.

"You mean you—"

"Yes, the donation was made under the condition that you never find out I was behind your being hired." He cast a mildly reproachful look at Mrs. Odell, who looked just as unrepentant as he did.

"Those things happen," she said.

"Indeed they do. Especially whenever Greg is involved." Christina stood on tiptoe and kissed him. "You're so pushy," she playfully chided. "Always trying to have your own way."

"Only when it matches your wishes," he said and escorted her under the shower of rice to the car. "The next project we work on together will involve a baby."

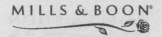

MILLS & BOON®

*M*akes
any time
special

Enjoy a romantic novel from
Mills & Boon®

Presents...™ *Enchanted*™ *Temptation*®

Historical Romance™ *Medical Romance*™

MILLS & BOON®

Next Month's Romance Titles

♡

Each month you can choose from a wide variety of romance novels from Mills & Boon®. Below are the new titles to look out for next month from the Presents...™ and Enchanted™ series.

Presents...™

A RELUCTANT MISTRESS	Robyn Donald
THE MARRIAGE RESOLUTION	Penny Jordan
THE FINAL SEDUCTION	Sharon Kendrick
THE REVENGE AFFAIR	Susan Napier
THE HIRED HUSBAND	Kate Walker
THE MILLIONAIRE AFFAIR	Sophie Weston
THE BABY VERDICT	Cathy Williams
THE IMPATIENT GROOM	Sara Wood

Enchanted™

THE DADDY DILEMMA	Kate Denton
AND MOTHER MAKES THREE	Liz Fielding
TO CLAIM A WIFE	Susan Fox
THE BABY WISH	Myrna Mackenzie
MARRYING A MILLIONAIRE	Laura Martin
THE HUSBAND CAMPAIGN	Barbara McMahon
TEMPTING A TYCOON	Leigh Michaels
MAIL-ORDER MARRIAGE	Margaret Way

On sale from 1st October 1999

H1 9909

Available at most branches of WH Smith, Tesco, Asda, Martins, Borders, Easons, Volume One/James Thin and most good paperback bookshops

FREE
4 BOOKS
AND A SURPRISE GIFT!

We would like to take this opportunity to thank you for reading this Mills & Boon® book by offering you the chance to take FOUR more specially selected titles from the Enchanted™ series absolutely FREE! We're also making this offer to introduce you to the benefits of the Reader Service™—

- ★ FREE home delivery
- ★ FREE monthly Newsletter
- ★ FREE gifts and competitions
- ★ Exclusive Reader Service discounts
- ★ Books available before they're in the shops

Accepting these FREE books and gift places you under no obligation to buy; you may cancel at any time, even after receiving your free shipment. Simply complete your details below and return the entire page to the address below. ***You don't even need a stamp!***

YES! Please send me 4 free Enchanted books and a surprise gift. I understand that unless you hear from me, I will receive 6 superb new titles every month for just £2.40 each, postage and packing free. I am under no obligation to purchase any books and may cancel my subscription at any time. The free books and gift will be mine to keep in any case.

N9EC

Ms/Mrs/Miss/Mr ....Initials ....
BLOCK CAPITALS PLEASE

Surname ....

Address ....

....

....Postcode ....

Send this whole page to:
UK: FREEPOST CN81, Croydon, CR9 3WZ
EIRE: PO Box 4546, Kilcock, County Kildare (stamp required)

Offer valid in UK and Eire only and not available to current Reader Service subscribers to this series. We reserve the right to refuse an application and applicants must be aged 18 years or over. Only one application per household. Terms and prices subject to change without notice. Offer expires 31st March 2000. As a result of this application, you may receive further offers from Harlequin Mills & Boon Limited and other carefully selected companies. If you would prefer not to share in this opportunity please write to The Data Manager at the address above.

Mills & Boon is a registered trademark owned by Harlequin Mills & Boon Limited.
Enchanted is being used as a trademark.

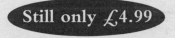
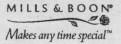